NINETEEN-S
BRITISH TELEVISION

A Quizbook

by

PAUL DONNELLEY

with drawings by Melanie Maude

PAUL WATKINS
STAMFORD
1998

.

DEDICATED TO JAYNE PRICE

My favourite 'production' of the '60s
Rwyn dy garu di nawr ac am byth

Typeset and published by
PAUL WATKINS
18, Adelaide Street, Stamford
Lincolnshire, PE9 2EN

ISBN
1 871615 82 8

Printed and bound by Woolnoughs of Irthlingborough

CONTENTS

Author's Preface	4
Foreword by Bob Monkhouse, OBE	5
Alphabetical Index of Quizzes	6
The Quizzes	9
The '60s TV Calendar	64
Further Reading	73
The Answers	77
Answers to Picture Quizzes	95

AUTHOR'S PREFACE

To many the Sixties were a golden age. Musically, we had The Beatles, Rolling Stones, Hendrix, Dylan, Beach Boys, the Kinks, the list is endless. Theatrically, the abolition of the Lord Chamberlain's Office saw the advent of *Hair* and *Oh! Calcutta*. In the cinema audiences flocked to *The Sound of Music, Mary Poppins, Oliver!, Dr No* and various *Carry on...* films. Politically, John Profumo resigned following his association with Christine Keeler, Harold Wilson became Prime Minister and Jeremy Thorpe said of Harold Macmillan's Cabinet reshuffle, 'Greater love hath no man than this, that he lay down his friends for his life'. In the sporting world England won the World Cup with Geoff Hurst scoring a hat-trick as we beat West Germany 4-2. Out of this world, Yuri Gagarin became the first man in space while Neil Armstrong became the first man to set foot on the moon. On the negative side, John F. Kennedy and Bobby Kennedy were both assassinated as was Dr Martin Luther King, Jr. Richard Nixon presided over the Vietnam War, actress Sharon Tate was butchered, and the Berlin Wall went up.

The Sixties were definitely a golden age as far as television is concerned as, I hope, this quizbook proves. This book features 102 quizzes on the stars and programmes of that decade. If you enjoy it, let me know and perhaps we'll go to a second volume. Or to one on the Seventies. You can e-mail me at 'paul@uk.com'.

My first debt of thanks goes to Graham McOwan who runs the excellent bookshop The Lighter Side (473 Upper Richmond Road West, East Sheen, London SW14. Tel: 0181 876 6045) for introducing me to my publisher, Shaun Tyas. Special thanks to Bob Monkhouse, OBE, for writing a fabulous foreword. Thanks also are due to Jeremy Beadle for his sagacious advice on all aspects of my career in the seventeen or so years I have known him. I owe a debt of gratitude to my assistant, Jennifer Clark.

Love and lust to the wonderful Sharon Hall who has nothing to do with this book but an awful lot to do with the life of its author.

The following have also been helpful in checking facts and supplying pictures: Geoffrey Bayldon, Honor Blackman, Anne Chamberlain (Python Productions Ltd), Matthew Corbett, Michaela Denis, Betty Driver, Norma Farnes (Eric Sykes Ltd), Keith Fordyce, Sheila Hancock, Gerald Harper, Frazer Hines, Bob Holness, the late Jimmy Jewel, Peter Jones, Bernard Levin, Francis Matthews, the late Frank Muir, Nicholas Parsons, Bill Pertwee, Shane Rimmer, Sir Jimmy Savile, Ned Sherrin, Valerie Singleton, Una Stubbs, M. R. Weir (National Viewers' & Listeners' Association), Alan Whicker, June Whitfield, Ernie Wise, OBE and Edward Woodward. I am particularly grateful to those who trusted me with valuable original photographs.   Paul Donnelley, 1998

FOREWORD

by Bob Monkhouse, OBE

Even the most fanatical Telly Addict will find this book a tough challenge. TV in the '60s? I *was* there but Paul Donnelley still is. His comprehensive knowledge of that TV decade can only mean that he's living in the past, unearthing fascinating facts in which lovers of nostalgia will revel.

With so many of the thirty-year-old shows popping up on our screens again and crowding the shelves of video shops, a whole new audience of youngsters can join their elders in competing to answer tricky questions about *Monty Python's Flying Circus, Dr Who, The Avengers, Randall & Hopkirk (Deceased)* and *Thunderbirds*.

I confess to being utterly stumped by many of these intriguing posers. Do you know why Private Walker ended up in *Dad's Army* instead of the proper one? The answer astonished me. Had you ever realised that the factory treasurer in *The Rag Trade* married Regan of *The Sweeney*? And that the man I replaced as host of *The Golden Shot* was a singing quizmaster whose mother-in-law was Thora Hird and who shared a wife with Mel Tormé? Oh, what memories! And what happy days!

So if you think you remember everything about *Blue Peter, Coronation Street* or *Crackerjack*, prepare to stun your family with your erudition. That's the quiz game aspect of this book. Personally, I just find it an endlessly fascinating reminder of the innocent pleasures of the past, from silly old *Crossroads* to black and white *Maigret*. So I'll be keeping my copy at my bedside as a bit of a browser, something to trigger off late-night recollections of Eric and Ernie, Dick Emery, Jess Yates, young David Frost, Tony Hancock, Harry H. Corbett, Sid James ... you get the idea.

Why have I written this foreword? Simply because the author asked me if I could. And I could never resist proving that I know the answer to a question like that. Oh, and a little tip: if you want to know the answers to the questions about me, buy my video *Bob Monkhouse Exposes Himself*. Apart from displaying what I really do for a living (rather racy cabaret!) and have never done on TV, it contains all my secrets, public and private.

Good viewing!

ALPHABETICAL INDEX OF QUIZZES

	Quiz number
Adam Adamant Lives!	Quiz 41
The Adventures of Robin Hood	Quiz 7
American Ragbag 1	Quiz 8
American Ragbag 2	Quiz 61
Gerry Anderson	Quiz 101
The Avengers 1	Quiz 13
The Avengers 2	Quiz 85
The Avengers 3	Quiz 89
Blue Peter	Quiz 58
Callan	Quiz 92
Call My Bluff	Quiz 98
Camberwick Green 1	Quiz 15
Camberwick Green 2	Quiz 81
Captain Pugwash	Quiz 36
Captain Scarlet and the Mysterons 1	Quiz 16
Captain Scarlet and the Mysterons 2	Quiz 43
Catchphrase	Quiz 33
Cathy Come Home	Quiz 57
Chigley	Quiz 14
The Clangers	Quiz 52
Commercial Break	Quiz 48
Compact	Quiz 95
Harry H. Corbett	Quiz 39
Coronation Street 1	Quiz 9
Coronation Street 2	Quiz 26
Coronation Street 3	Quiz 34
Coronation Street 4	Quiz 44
Coronation Street 5	Quiz 59
Crackerjack	Quiz 62
Crossroads	Quiz 21
Dad's Army 1	Quiz 5
Dad's Army 2	Quiz 49
Danger Man	Quiz 25
Richard Dimbleby	Quiz 6
Dixon of Dock Green	Quiz 40
Dr Finlay's Casebook	Quiz 23
Dr Who 1	Quiz 10
Dr Who 2	Quiz 53
Dr Who 3	Quiz 67

Dick Emery	Quiz 66
Eurovision Song Contest	Quiz 86
Face to Face	Quiz 74
Fireball XL5	Quiz 38
The Forsyte Saga	Quiz 97
Four Feather Falls	Quiz 65
David Frost	Quiz 96
The Golden Shot	Quiz 70
Tony Hancock	Quiz 22
It's A Knockout	Quiz 32
Sid James	Quiz 29
Joe 90	Quiz 37
The Likely Lads	Quiz 28
The Liver Birds	Quiz 83
Arthur Lowe	Quiz 69
The Magic Roundabout	Quiz 45
Magpie	Quiz 54
Maigret	Quiz 90
Bob Monkhouse	Quiz 76
Monty Python's Flying Circus 1	Quiz 19
Monty Python's Flying Circus 2	Quiz 47
Monty Python's Flying Circus 3	Quiz 55
Morecambe & Wise	Quiz 71
Name the Year 1	Quiz 1
Name the Year 2	Quiz 30
Nearest & Dearest	Quiz 64
David Nixon	Quiz 3
John Noakes	Quiz 99
Pat Phoenix	Quiz 60
Pinky & Perky	Quiz 4
Play School	Quiz 20
Please, Sir!	Quiz 56
The Prisoner	Quiz 31
Ragbag 1	Quiz 11
Ragbag 2	Quiz 18
Ragbag 3	Quiz 68
Ragbag 4	Quiz 77
Ragbag 5	Quiz 80
Ragbag 6	Quiz 88
The Rag Trade	Quiz 2
Randall & Hopkirk (Deceased)	Quiz 50
The Saga of Noggin the Nog	Quiz 12
The Saint	Quiz 72

Sooty	Quiz 79
Steptoe & Son	Quiz 73
Stingray 1	Quiz 75
Stingray 2	Quiz 87
Supercar	Quiz 91
Sykes	Quiz 100
That Was The Week That Was	Quiz 24
This Is Your Life	Quiz 51
Thunderbirds 1	Quiz 17
Thunderbirds 2	Quiz 27
Thunderbirds 3	Quiz 84
Till Death Us Do Part	Quiz 102
Top of the Pops	Quiz 93
The Troubleshooters	Quiz 46
Trumpton 1	Quiz 63
Trumpton 2	Quiz 94
Alan Whicker	Quiz 78
Mary Whitehouse	Quiz 82
Jess Yates	Quiz 35
Z Cars	Quiz 42

PICTURE QUIZ 1

He played a novel-writing detective married to a woman called Steve. Who is he?

QUIZ 1 – *NAME THE YEAR* 1

In what years did the following events happen?

1. Neil Armstrong walked on the moon
   The first colour ad on British TV – Bird's Eye peas
   Mary Jo Kopechne drowned at Chappaquiddick
   Monty Python's Flying Circus took to the air
   50p coin introduced

2. Radio Caroline began broadcasting
   House of the Rising Sun became number 1
   Liz Taylor married Richard Burton for the first time
   Crossroads opened for business
   BBC2 began broadcasting

3. Cathy Gale became the first *Avengers* girl
   Marilyn Monroe died
   Telstar, the communications satellite, was launched
   Fireball XL5 was first broadcast
   Steptoe & Son opened for business

4. John F. Kennedy elected President
   The first appearance of both *Coronation Street* and *Tales of the Riverbank*
   Elvis Presley reached number 1 with *It's Now Or Never*
   The first motorway restaurant opened on the M1
   Introduction of the MOT test

5. *Callan* first appeared on TV
   Crook Dr Emil Savundra crossed swords with David Frost on TV
   Radio 1 began broadcasting
   Dee Time first appeared on TV and Pan's People first appeared on *Top of the Pops*
   The first cashpoint machine opened

QUIZ 2 – THE RAG TRADE

1. In which factory was the show set?
2. Who played the owner?
3. Who created the show?
4. Who played Paddy, the shop steward?
5. Who were the only two members of the cast to appear in the 1970s remake?
6. What was the name of the factory foreman played by Reg Varney?
7. Who played the factory treasurer?
8. Which diminutive actress, an early *Carry on...* stalwart, played Little Lil?
9. What was Lil good at creating?
10. What was the show's catchphrase as voiced by Paddy?

QUIZ 3 – DAVID NIXON

1. Who was David Nixon's principal straight man in the 1940s?
2. Where was David Nixon born?
3. What was David Nixon's first major TV appearance?
4. Which TV show for children did he present?
5. Which popular puppet made his TV début on David Nixon's show?
6. Whom did David Nixon surprise when he hosted *This Is Your Life*?
7. Which rôle did he regularly play in *Cinderella*?
8. How many times did he marry?
9. Who was the orchestra leader on *The David Nixon Show*?
10. How many weeks did the show spend in the Top 20?

PICTURE QUIZ 2

Who is the above quiz-show host?

QUIZ 4 – *PINKY & PERKY*

1. Who wore which colour?
2. Which of the two always wore a hat?
3. What was their signature tune?
4. What kind of animal was Vera Vixen?
5. Who was the long-lashed cow that appeared on the show?
6. What was the TV station owned by Pinky & Perky?
7. Who was the show's guest cat?
8. What was the name of the show's musical frog?
9. Which Pinky & Perky presenter also appeared in *Z Cars*?
10. Which year saw Pinky & Perky presented to the royal family at the *Royal Variety Performance?*

QUIZ 5 – *DAD'S ARMY* 1

1. True or false: the theme music *Who Do You Think You Are Kidding Mr Hitler?* was a genuine W.W.2 song.
2. Who sang the theme tune?

3. Who was Mrs Fox?
4. What was the civilian occupation of Chief ARP Warden Hodges?
5. What was the name of Captain Mainwaring's oft-mentioned but never seen wife?
6. What did the CP1 stand for on the platoon's epaulettes?
7. Whose catchphrase was 'We're doomed, I tell 'e, doomed'?
8. In which town is the show set?
9. What is the name of Captain Mainwaring's arch-rival in the Eastgate Platoon?
10. Why didn't Private Walker go into the proper army?

QUIZ 6 – RICHARD DIMBLEBY

1. In 1961 who became the first member of the royal family to be interviewed on TV when quizzed by Richard Dimbleby?
2. To which statesman was Dimbleby's father political adviser?
3. To which country was Dimbleby sent as the BBC's first war correspondent?
4. Which heavyweight political programme did Dimbleby present from September 1955?
5. Which award did Dimbleby receive in 1959?
6. What 'local' radio show did Dimbleby front for many years?
7. Which Nazi concentration camp was Dimbleby the first reporter to enter?
8. What was the name of his family newspaper on which Dimbleby first worked?
9. Where was the memorial service held for Dimbleby?
10. What was the cause of Dimbleby's death?

QUIZ 7 – ADVENTURES OF ROBIN HOOD

How many *Robin Hood* characters can you find hidden in the grid which appears opposite? They are hidden horizontally, vertically, diagonally and backwards.

QUIZ 8 – AMERICAN RAGBAG 1

1. In *Star Trek* what is the Enterprise's registration number?
2. In *The Addams Family* what distinguished Gomez from every other attorney in America?
3. In *Bewitched* of what did Aunt Clara have a prized collection?
4. In one episode of *The Dick Van Dyke Show* how did Rob try to lull himself to sleep?
5. What was the name of the fort in *F Troop*?
6. What nickname was given to sitcom star Frances Lawrence?

W	E	L	A	D	A	N	A	L	A	E	S
S	I	R	W	I	L	L	I	A	M	L	E
I	B	L	I	T	T	L	E	J	O	H	N
K	N	C	L	O	D	J	B	X	M	R	E
C	F	T	S	S	E	O	Y	B	E	J	S
U	S	I	M	R	C	Z	E	K	I	N	C
T	A	T	E	A	U	A	L	I	E	P	H
R	M	A	I	D	M	A	R	I	O	N	A
A	U	T	O	S	F	K	M	L	D	V	L
I	C	Y	O	R	Y	P	O	N	E	N	W
R	H	E	I	T	W	A	Y	L	D	T	Q
F	S	S	H	E	R	I	F	F	W	D	R

7. How many castaways were there on *Gilligan's Island*?
8. What was the name of Eva Gabor's character in *Green Acres*?
9. Who lives at 1313 Mockingbird Lane?
10. How many stories were there in the *Naked City*?

QUIZ 9 – *CORONATION STREET* 1

1. Who created the show?
2. Whose was the first death on the Street?
3. True or false: the original names of the characters were taken from graves in a Manchester cemetery.
4. Who were the threesome famous for drinking in the snug of the Rover's Return?
5. What was Ken Barlow's brother's name?
6. Whom did he marry?
7. Who wrote the show's theme tune?
8. Which pop star played Stanley Fairclough?
9. Who were the first couple to marry?
10. Who played Minnie Caldwell's lodger Jed Stone?

QUIZ 10 – *DR WHO* 1

1. What planet does Dr Who come from?
2. What does TARDIS stand for?
3. What relative did the Doctor have with him in the early years?
4. From which planet do the Daleks come from?
5. Which 'BBC man' invented the Daleks?
6. Which future *Blue Peter* presenter was for a time one of the Doctor's assistants?
7. Which of Dr Who's enemies appeared in *The Invasion* and were filmed emerging from sewers and walking down the steps of St Paul's Cathedral?
8. In which year did Patrick Troughton replace William Hartnell?
9. What does UNIT stand for?
10. Who played Colonel (later Brigadier) Lethbridge-Stewart?

QUIZ 11 – RAGBAG 1

1. Who created *Not Only ... But Also ...*?
2. On which show did E. L. Wisty first appear?
3. Who were the two original team captains on *Call My Bluff*?
4. What was the name of the series of pictures in *Vision On*?
5. How did Shaw Taylor finish each episode of *Police 5*?
6. Who was the next door neighbour in *Hector's House*?
7. What was the name of Tintin's dog?
8. Who drove Ivor the Engine?
9. Which show began 'Here is a house, here is a door, windows, one, two, three, four'?
10. On which show did Janice Nicholls 'give it foive'?

QUIZ 12 – *THE SAGA OF NOGGIN THE NOG*

How many characters from *The Saga of Noggin the Nog* can you find hidden in the grid opposite? They are hidden horizontally, vertically and backwards.

QUIZ 13 – *THE AVENGERS* 1

1. From which show did *The Avengers* evolve?
2. Who played Dr David Keel?
3. What was the name of the character who temporarily replaced Dr Keel?
4. What was the name of the song released by Patrick Macnee and Honor Blackman?
5. Who played *Avengers* girl Venus Smith?

N	M	E	R	W	O	V	A	E	T	P	T
R	O	O	T	Y	A	Y	R	Z	H	G	E
N	O	G	G	I	N	T	H	E	N	O	G
C	A	R	B	E	T	I	T	R	Y	E	A
T	R	G	R	A	C	U	L	U	S	M	F
C	H	E	L	P	D	R	T	U	N	K	E
A	G	H	O	E	P	T	C	U	I	R	C
K	R	T	I	C	Y	A	H	R	A	Y	N
O	R	Y	T	F	E	L	D	E	N	G	I
O	L	A	F	T	H	E	N	A	B	L	R
N	F	M	L	I	N	T	K	T	R	A	P
T	H	O	R	N	O	G	S	O	N	A	D

6. Which wrestler was knocked unconscious by Honor Blackman while recording the episode *Mandrake*?
7. How did Emma Peel supposedly get her name?
8. Who originally played the controller of the cybernauts?
9. Who replaced him?
10. Who played Tara King?

QUIZ 14 – *CHIGLEY*

1. Who ran the biscuit factory?
2. Who owned the stately home?
3. Who was his butler?
4. What was the name of the steam engine?
5. Who ran the wharf?
6. In which county is Chigley?
7. Who created the series?
8. Who was the show's narrator?
9. How many episodes of *Chigley* were made?
10. How did each episode end?

QUIZ 15 – *CAMBERWICK GREEN* 1

1. Who wrote *Camberwick Green*?
2. How did each episode start?
3. Who narrated the series?
4. Who was the village gossip?
5. Who rode a penny farthing?
6. How many soldier boys lived in the fort?
7. What was the name of the fort?
8. What was PC McGarry's number?
9. What was the name of the puppy who lived in the post office?
10. In which county was *Camberwick Green* set?

QUIZ 16 – *CAPTAIN SCARLET AND THE MYSTERONS* 1

Rearrange the following characters with their real names:

1.	Captain Scarlet	a.	Edward Wilkie
2.	Colonel White	b.	Adam Svenson
3.	Captain Black	c.	Magnolia Jones
4.	Captain Blue	d.	Karen Wainwright
5.	Lieutenant Green	e.	Chan Kwan
6.	Melody Angel	f.	Paul Metcalfe
7.	Symphony Angel	g.	Seymour Griffiths
8.	Destiny Angel	h.	Juliette Pointon
9.	Harmony Angel	i.	Conrad Turner
10.	Doctor Fawn	j.	Charles Gray

QUIZ 17 – *THUNDERBIRDS* 1

1. How did the Tracy brothers get their names?
2. What is Brains's real name?
3. What kind of car does Lady Penelope own?
4. What is its licence plate?
5. Who is the sworn enemy of International Rescue?
6. Who is this enemy's half-brother?
7. From how many pods can *Thunderbird 2* choose from?
8. Who is the pilot of *Thunderbird 2*?
9. Who is the oldest of the Tracy brothers?
10. What happened to Mrs Tracy?

QUIZ 18 – RAGBAG 2

1. From which country did *Hector's House* hail?
2. Who played the title rôle in *Paul Temple*?
3. What kind of programme was presented by Barry Bucknell?
4. Who hosted *Ready, Steady, Go*?

PICTURE QUIZ 3 AND 4

3. She was one of the few people who met her Nemesis. Name her.
4. She went from East Ham to a farm and mimed all the way! Who is she?

———

5. Who became famous playing the zither?
6. Who hosted the pub entertainment show *Stars & Garters*?
7. Who were the husband and wife team famous for their wildlife documentaries?
8. Who became well-known for flexing his muscles to *Wheels Cha-Cha* on *Opportunity Knocks*?
9. Who was known as '*The Galloping Gourmet*'?
10. Who played Billy Bunter on TV?

QUIZ 19 – *MONTY PYTHON'S FLYING CIRCUS* 1

1. Who was the only American member of the Python team?
2. What is the title of the show's signature tune?
3. Who played the organ in the nude?
4. Who provided the cartoons?
5. What breed of parrot featured in the 'Dead Parrot Sketch'?
6. Who was the honorary female member of the team?
7. What was the exact date of the broadcast of the first show?
8. Who played the 'It's' Man?
9. Who first used the phrase 'And now for something completely different'?
10. In the 'Restaurant Sketch' who complained about a dirty fork?

QUIZ 20 – *PLAY SCHOOL*

1. Who created the show?
2. On which channel was the show first seen?
3. Which presenter was known for his miming skill?
4. What was the name.of the woolly bird?
5. Who was the rag doll?
6. What Saturday afternoon show was a spin-off from *Play School*?
7. Who was the first male presenter?
8. What shapes were the three windows on the show?
9. What was the name of the black doll?
10. Who were the two ursine characters?

QUIZ 21 – *CROSSROADS*

1. Who composed the show's theme tune?
2. What was the show's working title?
3. How many times did Meg marry?
4. Why was Meg sent to jail?
5. What were the first words uttered on the show?
6. And by whom?
7. What character was memorably portrayed by Ann George?
8. What was cloth-capped Benny's surname?
9. Who, in 1969, became Meg's partner in the motel?
10. Which member of the cast was confined to a wheelchair both in the series and in real life?

QUIZ 22 – TONY HANCOCK

1. What was Hancock's full name?
2. In *The Poison Pen Letters* who, in fact, was penning the horrible missives to Hancock?
3. Who played the doctor and nurse in *The Blood Donor*?
4. In which radio show did Hancock play a dummy's tutor?
5. What were the two addresses most associated with Hancock?
6. What was the name of the thriller Hancock was reading in *The Missing Page*?
7. Who played the Snide in *Hancock's Half Hour*?
8. What kind of hat did Hancock invariably wear?
9. How many times did Hancock marry?
10. In which city did Hancock commit suicide?

PICTURE QUIZ 5

This actor has been a wizard and The Crowman, but who is he?

QUIZ 23 – *DR FINLAY'S CASEBOOK*

1. What was the name of the good doctor's housekeeper?
2. How did she always answer the telephone?
3. Where was the series set?
4. Who wrote the original stories on which the series was based?
5. What was Dr Finlay's Christian name?
6. In which year was the series set?
7. Who owned the practice?
8. Who was the local midwife?
9. Who played Dr Finlay's would-be London partner?
10. What kind of car did Dr Finlay drive?

QUIZ 24 – *THAT WAS THE WEEK THAT WAS*

1. Who was the show's producer-director?
2. Who sang the signature tune?
3. Which scriptwriter and future Labour MP produced for the show a list of 13 silent MPs – members who hadn't spoken in the House for ten years?
4. By what abbreviation was the show known?
5. Which member of the team was thumped by an irate husband following a vitriolic newspaper review of his wife's one-woman show?

19

6. Why did the BBC take the show off?
7. Which one of the following did *not* write for the show? Keith Waterhouse, John Cleese, Willis Hall, Richard Ingrams, Brian Glanville, Jack Rosenthal, Dennis Potter.
8. Who sang a calypso every week?
9. Who was the first choice for the main presenter's rôle?
10. How many times did the show top the television ratings?

QUIZ 25 – *DANGER MAN*

1. For whom did John Drake work in the first series?
2. In which city were the opening credits filmed?
3. Who did the voice-over at the start of each show?
4. Who created John Drake?
5. How many affairs did Drake have in the course of the series?
6. From the second series what was the show called in America?
7. Which future Labour MP appeared in an episode called *Not So Jolly Roger*?
8. What is the registration number of Drake's car?
9. What is used as a front for the organisation for whom Drake worked?
10. For whom did Drake work from series two?

QUIZ 26 – *CORONATION STREET* 2

1. Who ended up in the cells after a drunken night out with the darts team?
2. Who moved out of the Street in May 1963 after winning £5,000 on the Premium Bonds?
3. Who owned Gamma Garments?
4. Who were the first home owners in the Street?
5. Where was Bet Lynch's first job?
6. Who appeared as Elizabeth I in a Christmas 1966 fancy dress party?
7. Who was buried in the rubble following a train crash from the viaduct?
8. How did Elsie Tanner's wedding to Steve Tanner end?
9. What happened to Ken Barlow's brother following his emigration in 1968?
10. What was the name of the Street's early nightclub?

QUIZ 27 – *THUNDERBIRDS* 2

1. In what year is the series set?
2. How fast can *Thunderbird 1* fly?
3. Who provided the voice of Scott Tracy?
4. Which brother wore a lilac sash?

5. Which brother worked for WASP (the organisation that employs *Stingray*)?
6. Which brother is in love with Tin-Tin?
7. Which brother attended the Denver School of Advanced Technology?
8. What is Lady Penelope's surname?
9. For what did Parker spend time in jail?
10. Who provided the voice of Lady Penelope?

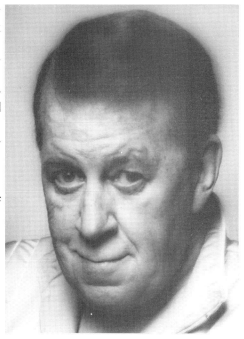

PICTURE QUIZ 6

This '60s TV presenter went 'on the beat'. Who is he?

QUIZ 28 – THE LIKELY LADS

1. Where did Bob and Terry work?
2. What were their surnames?
3. Where was the show set?
4. On what cartoon character was Bob an expert?
5. In the last episode what did Bob want to join?
6. What happened?
7. Who played Bob and Terry?
8. Who created the show?
9. For realism, what was unusual (for TV) about the pub scenes?
10. What was the sequel called?

QUIZ 29 – SID JAMES

1. Where was Sid born?
2. What was the name of the sitcom in which Sid co-starred with Peggy Mount?
3. What were their professions in the show?
4. In what sport was Sid a professional?
5. In what film did he make his début?
6. In which year did he leave *Hancock's Half Hour*?

21

7. What was his first *Carry On ...*?
8. In how many of the *Carry On ...* films did Sid appear?
9. In which sitcom did he play a champion of the underdog?
10. Who played his wife in *Bless This House*?

QUIZ 30 – NAME THE YEAR 2

In what years did the following events happen?

1. The first Identikit picture was issued
   Gagarin became the first man in space
   Helen Shapiro hit Number 1 with 'Walking Back to Happiness'
   Songs of Praise first appeared on TV
   West Side Story won Best Picture Oscar

2. First edition of *It's A Knockout*
   England won the World Cup
   Patrick Troughton became Dr Who
   John Lennon said the Beatles were more popular than Jesus
   Till Death Us Do Part first appeared on TV

3. The Milk Tray man appeared in a TV ad for the first time
   Cliff Richard represented the U.K. in Eurovision with *Congratulations*
   Tony Hancock committed suicide
   The Goon Show first appeared on TV
   Morecambe & Wise joined the BBC

4. First appearance of *Call My Bluff*
   The Rolling Stones got to number 1 with *(I Can't Get No) Satisfaction*
   Richard Dimbleby died
   The home video recorder was first marketed
   Thunderbirds blasted off

5. John Profumo resigned after lying to the House of Commons
   Hugh Gaitskell died aged 56
   Cliff Richard and the Shadows got to number 1 with *Summer Holiday*
   The Beeching Report on the railways was published
   Dr Who first appeared on TV

QUIZ 31 – *THE PRISONER*

1. In which village was the show filmed?
2. What number was assigned to The Prisoner?
3. What car is driven in the opening sequence?

PICTURE QUIZ 7

We all know that this is Harry Corbett, with Sooty and Sweep, but who is the puppet in the middle?

4. Which future TV lawyer appeared as one of the Number 2s?
5. Where was the show set?
6. Who played The Prisoner?
7. What is the name of The Prisoner Appreciation Society?
8. What was The Prisoner's real name?
9. When is The Prisoner's birthday?
10. What was the title of the last episode of the show?

QUIZ 32 – IT'S A KNOCKOUT

1. Who were the original presenters?
2. Who won the first competition? Was it (a) Blackpool (b) Bournemouth or (c) Bognor?
3. What was the name of the international version?
4. Who was the British referee?
5. Who were the two international referees?
6. What was the name given to the marathon in the international version?
7. Which presenter was famous for his laugh?
8. In which year did the show begin?
9. What was the short-running American version of the show called?
10. Who were the three team captains on It's a Royal Knockout?

PICTURE QUIZ 8

Who is this television
personality, well known
as the founder of the
National Viewers and
Listeners Association?

QUIZ 33 – CATCHPHRASE

With which famous TV personalities are the following catchphrases
associated?
1.   'Hello, good evening and welcome'
2.   'Boom! Boom!'
3.   'Tatty-bye'
4.   'Hello, honky-tonks'
5.   'Pin back yer lugholes'
6.   'Dodgy!'
7.   'She knows, y'know'
8.   'Nay, nay and thrice nay'
9.   'I mean that most sincerely folks'
10. 'I'm in charge!'

What were the real names of Morecambe & Wise?

QUIZ 34 – *CORONATION STREET* 3

1. Who was the lay preacher at the Glad Tidings Mission?
2. What is the name of the street that runs at the top end of Coronation Street?
3. What degree did Ken Barlow achieve?
4. Why was Ken Barlow jailed in 1967?
5. When the Barlow twins were born, who was the heavier?
6. In which year did Emily Bishop pass her driving test?
7. What was Minnie Caldwell's husband's name?
8. Who is Gordon Clegg's mother?
9. Where was Len Fairclough's yard?
10. What was Hilda Ogden's maiden name?

PICTURE QUIZ 10

In which sport did Jimmy Savile excel as a professional?

QUIZ 35 – JESS YATES

1. What was the nickname given to Jess Yates during his time on *Stars On Sunday*?
2. Where was Jess Yates born?
3. What was his first job?
4. Which movie company for kids did Jess Yates have a hand in forming?
5. For which two pools companies did he create female choirs?
6. On which long-running variety show did Jess Yates work for its first three years?
7. Following his marriage, what profession did Jess Yates enter?
8. What was the age gap between Jess Yates and actress Anita Kay which caused a scandal in 1974?
9. What was the BAFTA-award-winning children's show about history devised by Jess Yates?
10. Who replaced Jess Yates as host of *Stars On Sunday* on the week following his dismissal?

QUIZ 36 – *CAPTAIN PUGWASH*

1. What was the name of the good captain's ship?
2. Who was his arch enemy?
3. What was the name of the cabin boy?
4. Who provided the voices?
5. Who created the show?
6. What was the title of the show's theme tune?
7. What was the name of Pugwash's first mate?
8. Who were the able seamen?
9. Whose ingenuity usually got the captain out of scrapes?
10. What was the similar animation series also created by the man who gave us *Captain Pugwash*?

QUIZ 37 – *JOE 90*

1. What is Joe's surname?
2. How old is he?
3. Joe's father created BIG RAT. What do the initials stand for?
4. Who provided the voice for Joe's father?
5. For which organisation does Joe work?
6. Who was Shane Weston's deputy?
7. Where does Joe hide his secret agent equipment?
8. What is the name of Joe's father's housekeeper?
9. Why does Joe only wear glasses on missions?
10. How does the last episode end?

QUIZ 38 – *FIREBALL XL5*

1. In what year is the series set?
2. Who commands *Fireball XL5*?
3. What is the name of the ship's doctor?
4. How long is the ship?
5. What is the name of its resident pet alien creature?
6. What name was given to the ship's detachable nose cone?
7. For which sector of space is *Fireball XL5* responsible?
8. Who is Commander Zero's assistant?
9. What is unusual about the ship's co-pilot?
10. Who is the ship's navigator?

QUIZ 39 – HARRY H. CORBETT

1. What did the H stand for?
2. Why did he add the initial?
3. Where was he born?
4. What was his father's occupation?
5. With which actress's theatre workshop did he appear in the 1950s?

6. What was the name of the sitcom that followed *Steptoe & Son* in which Corbett starred?
7. Which honour was given Corbett in the 1976 New Year Honours List?
8. Who was Corbett's first wife?
9. In which *Carry on ...* did he play Detective Sergeant Bung?
10. How tall was he?

QUIZ 40 – *DIXON OF DOCK GREEN*

1. What was Dixon's son-in-law's name?
2. What was Dixon's first name?
3. In which film did Dixon first appear?
4. What was Dixon's catchphrase?
5. What was the title of the show's theme tune?
6. Where was Dixon standing at the start of each episode?
7. Who created the series?
8. What was the name of Dixon's daughter?
9. How many episodes were made? Was it (a) 429 (b) 587 or (c) 626?
10. Which comedy actor played Tom Carr, a bent copper, in an episode called *The Rotten Apple*?

QUIZ 41 – *ADAM ADAMANT LIVES!*

1. To what age did Adam Adamant belong?
2. Who played his mini-skirted sidekick Georgina Jones?
3. What was Adam Adamant's full name?
4. Who was his arch enemy?
5. What happened to Adam in 1902?
6. Who took the title rôle?
7. Which real-life newsreader appeared as himself in an episode of the show?
8. Which future film director, famous for *Blade Runner*, took charge of one episode?
9. With which weapon was Adam less than a master?
10. How many episodes of the show were made?

QUIZ 42 – *Z CARS*

1. Who played Fancy Smith?
2. Where was *Z Cars* set?
3. Which two actors defected to *Softly Softly*?
4. Who played Bert Lynch?
5. How did Troy Kennedy Martin conceive the idea for the show?
6. Which future Oscar winner walked the beat?
7. The signature tune was adopted from which folk song?

PICTURE QUIZ 11

Just a minute! This TV presenter has been a straight man to Benny Hill, Arthur Haynes and numerous other comedians. Who is he?

8. Which future *Eastender* played Mick Quilley?
9. Who was the nick's resident bully?
10. What were the call signs of the two patrol cars?

QUIZ 43 – *CAPTAIN SCARLET AND THE MYSTERONS* 2

1. What does S.P.V. stand for?
2. What was unusual about driving the S.P.V.?
3. From where do the Mysterons hail?
4. What was the name of the fateful mission led by Captain Black?
5. Which member of Spectrum attended West Point Military Academy?
6. Who provided the voice for Captain Scarlet?
7. Which member of Spectrum is an ex-jailbird?
8. Who provided the voice of the Mysterons?
9. What are the two Mysteron 'circles' supposed to represent?
10. What is the name given to Captain Scarlet's ability to bring himself back to life after normally fatal wounds?

PICTURE QUIZ 12

This, of course, is Alan Whicker. When was *Whicker's World* first broadcast?

QUIZ 44 – *CORONATION STREET* 4

1. Who accused Ena Sharples of writing poison pen letters?
2. What relation was Albert Tatlock to Ken Barlow?
3. What was Betty Turpin's first husband's profession?
4. Who spoke the first words on the first show?
5. When a fractured gas main caused the evacuation of the Street to the Glad Tidings Mission, what did Jack Walker take with him?
6. How many children did the Ogdens have?
7. For what football team did David Barlow play?
8. Who was the first baby born in the Street?
9. Why did Ken Barlow's affair with Marion Lund flounder?
10. Who wrote a letter to Prince Philip over the local council's proposal to rename the Street Florida Street?

D	L	E	D	U	R	T	N	I	M	R	E
B	Y	R	N	E	H	C	A	M	R	M	J
Z	E	L	X	O	P	D	O	U	G	A	L
S	V	W	A	T	Y	U	B	M	L	G	G
E	L	J	T	N	M	V	X	Z	Y	A	S
Z	Q	F	L	O	R	E	N	C	E	E	B
E	M	O	H	D	R	F	I	U	M	I	O
B	A	D	O	L	U	A	P	H	K	L	R
E	M	F	B	A	S	I	L	D	V	A	A
D	I	H	U	K	T	D	M	O	A	S	I
E	A	V	D	I	Y	H	F	H	M	O	Y
E	M	H	S	K	D	A	N	A	I	R	B

QUIZ 45 – *THE MAGIC ROUNDABOUT*

How many characters from *The Magic Roundabout* can you find in the grid?

QUIZ 46 – *THE TROUBLESHOOTERS*

1. What was the show's alternative title?
2. What were the names of the Troubleshooters?
3. What was the name of the rival company?
4. Who was president of that board?
5. Who played him?
6. What was the name of the financial wizard?
7. What was the model for the show?
8. What position was held by Brian Stead?
9. Who wrote the signature tune?
10. On whom was the MP Joan Marple reputedly based?

31

PICTURE QUIZ 13

Two difficult, but necessary, questions for this one: (a) What is the origin of the name 'Monty Python'? (b) What is the name of the theme tune?

QUIZ 47 – *MONTY PYTHON'S FLYING CIRCUS* 2

1. In the 'Barber Sketch' why is the barber (Bevis) afraid of cutting hair?
2. What did the barber always want to be?
3. What peculiar physical abnormality was suffered by Arthur Frampton?
4. Which chocolate manufacturer made sweets with names like Crunchy Frog, Cockroach Cluster and Anthrax Ripple?
5. Which TV executive was mentioned in the 'Buying a Bed' sketch?
6. What name was given to the gang of old ladies who rode motorcycles and terrorised people?
7. Who played Jimmy Buzzard, the extremely stupid footballer who is only capable of three sentences?
8. How many Upper Class Twit of the Year contests had been held prior to the one televised on the show?
9. Why does the Minister of Silly Walks arrive late?
10. What was the name of the large hedgehog who was believed to be following Dinsdale Piranha?

MYSTERY EXTRA QUESTION

And just before the commercial break, have a think about this one! Were daleks left- or right-handed? Answer when we get back.

END OF PART ONE

QUIZ 48 – A COMMERCIAL BREAK

1. In 1962 Terry Brooks became the first in a line of blond, blue-eyed chocolate box heroes. What particular product did he advertise?
2. Who played Katie in the Oxo ads for eighteen years?
3. Which beer 'works wonders'?
4. Which DJ claimed Omo added 'brightness to cleanness and whiteness'?
5. About which sweets did kids say 'wotalotigot'?
6. Who promoted Camay, despite the fact that it caused an allergic reaction to her face until the company changed the formula?
7. Who urged the country to 'go to work on an egg'?
8. Who informed us that Homepride's 'graded grains make finer flour'?
9. Which petrol company told drivers to put a tiger in their tank?
10. Who was the actor who was never alone with a Strand?

PART TWO

All daleks had their arm on their right and their gun on their left. This means that they were right-handed. Any photograph or drawing which shows the opposite has simply been incompetently printed the wrong way round (which does sometimes happen).

QUIZ 49 – *DAD'S ARMY 2*

1. Who was always asking to be excused?
2. What was Private Pike's first name?
3. What was Hodges's nickname for Captain Mainwaring?
4. What was the name of the verger?
5. Apart from Pike and Walker, who was the only member of the platoon not to have won any military honours?
6. Which member of the platoon was an undertaker?
7. Whose van did the platoon use for transport?
8. Who had fought the fuzzy-wuzzies?
9. Who worked at the Army & Navy stores before his retirement?
10. Why did Pike call Sergeant Wilson 'Uncle Arthur'?

QUIZ 50 – *RANDALL & HOPKIRK (DECEASED)*

1. How did Marty Hopkirk die?
2. What was the show's title in America?
3. Who was rumoured to be originally intended for the rôle of Jeff Randall?
4. What was the name of Marty's widow?
5. For how long must Marty walk the earth as a ghost?
6. How many people can see and hear Marty?
7. Where was Marty's flat?
8. What was the inscription on Marty's gravestone?
9. What was Jeff Randall's original name?
10. In which episode did Jeff briefly appear as a ghost?

QUIZ 51 – *THIS IS YOUR LIFE*

1. Who was the first honoured guest of the show?
2. Who originally created the show?
3. When Eamonn Andrews was the honoured guest for the second time, who presented the show?
4. Who was the first guest to be honoured twice?
5. Who was the last honoured guest of the '60s?
6. In which year did the show leave the BBC for the first time?
7. Who were the only two people to refuse to be honoured?
8. Who composed the theme tune?
9. Who was intended to be the first honoured guest?
10. Who was the first 'royal' honoured guest?

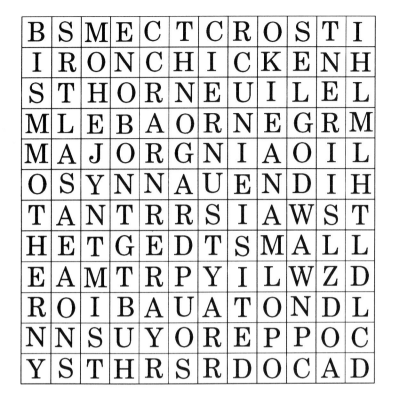

B	S	M	E	C	T	C	R	O	S	T	I
I	R	O	N	C	H	I	C	K	E	N	H
S	T	H	O	R	N	E	U	I	L	E	L
M	L	E	B	A	O	R	N	E	G	R	M
M	A	J	O	R	G	N	I	A	O	I	L
O	S	Y	N	N	A	U	E	N	D	I	H
T	A	N	T	R	R	S	I	A	W	S	T
H	E	T	G	E	D	T	S	M	A	L	L
E	A	M	T	R	P	Y	I	L	W	Z	D
R	O	I	B	A	U	A	T	O	N	D	L
N	N	S	U	Y	O	R	E	P	P	O	C
Y	S	T	H	R	S	R	D	O	C	A	D

QUIZ 52 – *THE CLANGERS*

Find nine characters from the popular children's series in the grid.

QUIZ 53 – *DR WHO 2*

1. Who played Dr Who's assistant Jamie McCrimmon?
2. Who played Ian Chesterton in the first series?
3. Why is the TARDIS a police box?
4. Who composed the theme tune?
5. What was the title of the very first *Dr Who* story?
6. What was the date of the first broadcast?
7. Who released a single entitled *I'm Going to Spend my Christmas with a Dalek*?
8. Which '60s pop group made a fleeting appearance in *The Chase*?
9. What is the name of the method by which the Doctor changes his appearance?
10. Who was the Doctor when his face appeared on the opening titles for the first time?

Who is this *Avengers* actress?

QUIZ 54 – *MAGPIE*

1. According to the theme tune what did 1 represent?
2. Who were the first three presenters?
3. How many presenters worked on the show during the show's run?
4. Which presenter's brother became a Tory MP?
5. Which presenter appeared as 'a typical teenager' on the first edition of *Juke Box Jury*?
6. In which year did *Magpie* begin?
7. When did the show end?
8. According to the theme tune what did 7 stand for?
9. A regular section was called 'A Date with Tony'. Who presented it and what was it about?
10. Which TV company produced the show?

QUIZ 55 – *MONTY PYTHON'S FLYING CIRCUS* 3

1. How tall is Mr Howard Stools?
2. With which hymn do the Church Police make an arrest?
3. What job does Mr Anchovy want to do?

38

What is the name of the actor who played Adam Adamant?

4. Why?
5. To which job is he best suited?
6. Why was the dead parrot sitting on its perch in the first place?
7. Which tasty pink meat dish was made into the subject of a song by the team?
8. What is the name of the dangerous sheep?
9. How many votes did Kevin Phillips Bong (the silly candidate) receive?
10. What is in the brown paper bag planted on a suspect by PC Thatcher?

QUIZ 56 – *PLEASE SIR!*

1. What class did Mr Hedges (John Alderton) teach in the series?
2. Who was the class 'mummy's boy'?
3. What was Mr Hedges's nickname?
4. In which branch of the army did caretaker Potter serve?
5. Who wanted to become a nun?
6. Who originally played Sharon Eversleigh?
7. Which character was played by Peter Cleall?
8. Who was the animal lover?

9. What was the name of the deputy headmistress?
10. What was the name of the spin-off show following John Alderton's departure?

QUIZ 57 – *CATHY COME HOME*

1. Who played the two lead rôles?
2. Who wrote the play on which the show was based?
3. Who was the director?
4. What was unusual about the play?
5. Which organisation for the homeless took its impetus from the show?
6. Who said of the show, 'I would like it to be compulsory viewing once a month for the next five years'?
7. How did Cathy get to London?
8. How many children did Cathy and Ray have?
9. In which year was *Cathy Come Home* first broadcast?
10. What was Ray's occupation?

QUIZ 58 – *BLUE PETER*

1. In which year was Petra born?
2. What was the name of Petra's son, looked after on the show by John Noakes?
3. Which member of the team took a lion called Valentine for a walk?
4. When did the show go twice-weekly?
5. What was unusual about the show's pet tortoise Fred?
6. When and to where was the show's first summer expedition?
7. What is the name of the *Blue Peter* theme tune?
8. What was the name of the first *Blue Peter* cat?
9. Which member of the team climbed 127ft up HMS *Ganges* to almost become the button boy?
10. What was the name of the elephant which disgraced itself in the studio in 1969?

QUIZ 59 – *CORONATION STREET* 5

1. What was Minnie Caldwell's cat called?
2. For which organisation did Frank Barlow work prior to his retirement?
3. What was the name of Valerie Tatlock's hairdressing salon?
4. What was the real name of 'pop star' Brett Falcon?
5. Who threw a race with Len Fairclough in March 1964 to allow Len to save face?

PICTURE QUIZ 16

Frazer Hines in his famous role from *Dr Who*. What is the name of the Scottish character he played?

6. Who discovered an unexploded bomb in Albert Tatlock's backyard?
7. Why was Jack Walker charged with selling drinks after hours?
8. Who was fined £5 for driving the wrong way down a one-way street?
9. What caused the death of Ena Sharples's daughter?
10. When Len was elected a councillor in September 1966 whom did he beat on the toss of a coin?

QUIZ 60 – PAT PHOENIX

1. Where was Pat Phoenix born?
2. What was her real name?
3. How did she come by her stage name?
4. Identify the *Coronation Street* co-star she married on Christmas Eve 1972.

5. In which year did Pat Phoenix leave *Coronation Street* for the first time?
6. Who described Pat Phoenix as 'Catherine of all the bleeding Russias'?
7. What was the name of the sitcom Pat Phoenix starred in after leaving the Street?
8. True or false: Pat Phoenix was a non-smoker in real life.
9. To which political party did Pat give vociferous support?
10. What is the connection between Pat Phoenix and *Till Death Us Do Part*?

QUIZ 61 – AMERICAN RAGBAG 2

1. In *The Brady Bunch* the cast appeared in a noughts-and-crosses board in the opening titles. Who appeared where?
2. Who played the ghost in *The Ghost & Mrs Muir*?
3. How has Dave Crabtree's mother been reincarnated?
4. With what words did Batman's butler answer the phone?
5. Which brilliant criminal lawyer enjoyed eating at McQuade's Bar & Grill?
6. What nickname was given to Gerald Lloyd Kookson III in *77 Sunset Strip*?
7. What kind of animal was Cecil in *The Beany & Cecil Show*?
8. How was Barbara Stanwyck listed in the credits of *The Big Valley*?
9. Name two of Ben Cartwright's three sons in *Bonanza*.
10. In what year was *The Flintstones* set?

QUIZ 62 – *CRACKERJACK*

1. Who was the first host?
2. What was the name of the quiz in which wrong answers were rewarded with a cabbage?
3. At what time and on what day of the week was the show broadcast?
4. Which member of the team was an understudy to the Crazy Gang?
5. Which of the following was not a *Crackerjack* girl:
    (a) Frances Barlow (b) Lesley Judd (c) Jillian Comber or (d) Pip Hunter?
6. Which *Crackerjack* host was a regular on *The Black and White Minstrel Show*?
7. Who were the show's first two regular comics?
8. Which *Crackerjack* girl had an unsuccessful pop career as Kristine Sparkle?
9. What was given to all contestants – winners and losers – on the show?
10. What did the audience shout every time someone said the show's title?

PICTURE QUIZ 17

Bernard Levin is famous for his television and newspaper journalism, interviews and reviews; but who is his favourite composer of music?

QUIZ 63 – *TRUMPTON* 1

Match up the following inhabitants of Trumpton with their correct job:

1.	Philby	a.	window cleaner
2.	Mr Robinson	b.	telephone engineer
3.	Chippy Minton	c.	flower seller
4.	Nick Fisher	d.	fireman
5.	Mr Antonio	e.	ice cream man
6.	Mrs Cobbit	f.	mayor's chauffeur
7.	Mr Wantage	g.	town clerk
8.	Mr Troop	h.	bill poster
9.	Barney McGrew	i.	printer
10.	Mr Munnings	j.	carpenter

QUIZ 64 – NEAREST & DEAREST

1. What was the name of the pickle factory run by Nellie and Eli?
2. Who played Nellie and Eli?
3. What was Nellie and Eli's relationship?
4. About whom did Nellie enquire 'Has he been?'
5. Who played him?
6. Who was the factory foreman?
7. Who played Lily?
8. True or false: Nellie was a malapropist.
9. Which television company made the show?
10. Who created *Nearest & Dearest*?

QUIZ 65 – FOUR FEATHER FALLS

1. What did the four feathers do?
2. Who provided the voice of Tex Tucker?
3. Who provided the singing voice of Tex Tucker?
4. What was the name of the bandit?
5. Identify Tex's horse and dog.
6. Who ran the town saloon?
7. What was the saloon called?
8. In which state was the series set?
9. Who owned the general store?
10. What was the name of the renegade Indian chief?

QUIZ 66 – DICK EMERY

1. What was the profession of Dick's parents?
2. What was the name of the man-made female who stated, 'Ooh, you are awful – but I like you!'?
3. True or false: Dick did not suffer from nerves before a performance.
4. In whose show did Dick make his début as a female impersonator?
5. At which London theatre was Dick a regular for almost a year in the 1940s?
6. Who was the spinster character who asked men, 'Are you married?'
7. What did Dick say as the bovver boy when he made a mistake?
8. What was the name of Dick's tramp character?
9. How many times did Dick marry?
10. What was the name of the lecherous oddjob man who was a constant burden to his family?

P	U	B	A	R	B	A	R	A	D	K	I
O	T	U	T	N	E	M	R	E	B	Y	C
L	J	S	S	E	N	S	O	R	I	T	E
L	U	M	O	R	O	K	S	M	T	R	W
Y	E	T	I	L	S	D	A	V	X	E	A
M	N	L	P	A	J	A	M	I	E	K	R
S	I	D	Z	H	C	L	O	C	R	A	R
O	Z	O	E	C	N	E	R	T	O	M	I
R	H	D	N	U	O	K	P	O	N	Y	O
V	A	O	T	S	A	S	H	R	S	O	R
A	E	Z	A	R	B	I	O	I	R	T	S
D	E	L	O	S	S	T	H	A	L	S	X

QUIZ 67 – *DR WHO* 3

How many characters can you find in the grid? Look vertically, horizontally and diagonally.

QUIZ 68 – RAGBAG 3

1. Who were the husband and wife team famous for their underwater films?
2. Who was the hostess on *Double Your Money*?
3. Which TV prankster wrote a best-selling guide to public lavatories?
4. Who, in July 1966, said, 'There are some people on the pitch, they think it's all over ... it is now!'?
5. Who was chairman of *Going for a Song*?
6. Who was the storyteller on *Blue Peter*?
7. What was the real name of Sabrina?
8. In which TV series did Frank Marker appear?
9. Who hosted *It's a Square World*?
10. Which crossword quiz show was hosted by Bob Holness?

QUIZ 69 – ARTHUR LOWE

1. What was the name of the character Arthur played in *Coronation Street*?
2. What was Arthur's original career ambition?
3. At what age did he become an actor?
4. What was the name of the series that was a spin-off from his *Coronation Street* character?
5. Who was the priest he played in *Bless Me, Father*?
6. What was his profession in *A. J. Wentworth, B.A.*?
7. In which county was Arthur born?
8. In which decade did he join the *Street*?
9. Of which cartoon series, created by Roger Hargreaves, was Arthur the narrator?
10. What was Arthur's military rank during World War II?

QUIZ 70 – *THE GOLDEN SHOT*

1. What was the nationality of the show's first host, Jackie Rae?
2. In which year did the show first appear on TV?
3. From which country did the show originate?
4. Name two of the original three hostesses.
5. On what day of the week did the show originally go out?
6. Identify the man responsible for positioning the crossbow at the end of the show.
7. Who was the show's last host?
8. What was the name of the hostess who counted on her fingers?
9. Which TV company produced the show?
10. Who originally replaced Bob Monkhouse as host?

QUIZ 71 – MORECAMBE & WISE

1. Who was the older – Eric or Ernie?
2. What were their real surnames?
3. When did they first team up?
4. What was the name of their unsuccessful first TV show?
5. What did Eric call André Previn?
6. Which singer lost her shoes on the show and ended up wearing hobnail boots?
7. Which horror film star frequently appeared but never got paid?
8. How many films did the duo make?
9. Which Oscar-winning actress appeared in one of Ernie's famous plays as Cleopatra and recited the line 'Beauty like what I have got'?
10. Who was the lady who appeared at the end of the show to thank the audience for watching 'Me and my little show'?

PICTURE QUIZ 18

In the 1970s she co-starred with Terry Scott in their own show. In the 1960s she appeared in Tony Hancock's 'The Blood Donor' as a nurse. Who is she?

QUIZ 72 – *THE SAINT*

1. What was the number plate of Simon Templar's car?
2. Who mostly played Chief Inspector Claude Eustace Teal?
3. What kind of car did Simon Templar drive?
4. Who wrote the original novels on which the series was based?
5. What was on *The Saint's* calling card?
6. How tall was Simon Templar?
7. Who was the first choice to play Simon Templar?
8. Which future *Bond* girl and *Avenger* character appeared as Pauline Stone in an episode called *The Arrow of God*?
9. Which one of the following future *Coronation Street* stars never appeared in *The Saint*: (a) Mark Eden (b) Patrick Troughton (c) Johnny Briggs (d) Shane Rimmer (e) Leonard Sachs or (f) Bernard Youens?
10. Who owns the rights to *The Saint*?

PICTURE QUIZ 19

The producer-director of *That Was The Week That Was* and associate producer of *Tonight*. Who is he?

QUIZ 73 – *STEPTOE & SON*

1. What was the name of the family horse?
2. What went wrong when Albert taught Harold to dance?
3. Who created the show?
4. In which part of London was the show set?
5. Under what umbrella title was the first show broadcast?
6. What did Albert dunk in *The Bath* in the episode of that name?
7. Which TV mogul reputedly banned the show from his home?
8. What hung to the right of the desk in the Steptoes' living room?
9. How did Harold often disparagingly refer to Albert?
10. What stuffed animal wore a hat in the living room?

48

QUIZ 74 – *FACE TO FACE*

1. Who hosted the show?
2. Who was reduced to tears on the show?
3. Why?
4. What was unusual about the host?
5. To which country did the host later become U.K. Ambassador?
6. Of which TV company was the host Chairman for thirteen years?
7. Which magazine did the host edit from 1961 to 1965?
8. Which American show inspired *Face to Face*?
9. How many subjects of *Face to Face* were women?
10. When the show was revived, who was the interrogator?

QUIZ 75 – *STINGRAY* 1

1. With what words did each show begin?
2. Who sang the 'Marina' theme tune?
3. Who piloted *Stingray*?
4. Stingray was operated by WASP. What did the initials stand for?
5. What was the real name of Phones?
6. Who was WASP's arch enemy?
7. Who was the hoverchair-bound commander of WASP?
8. With whom was his daughter Atlanta secretly in love?
9. What number was printed on *Stingray*'s stern?
10. How many sting missiles did *Stingray* carry?

QUIZ 76 – BOB MONKHOUSE

1. From whom did Bob take over as host of *The Golden Shot*?
2. What type of character did Bob play in *The Big Noise*?
3. Which prestigious show did Bob host from a famous London theatre?
4. Of which show, later presented by, among others, Jonathan Routh, was Bob the first host?
5. What was the name of Bob's co-writer, who later committed suicide?
6. What show, presented by Bob, reflected his love of old movies?
7. In which *Carry on ...* film did Bob star?
8. Which award did Bob receive shortly after his 65th birthday?
9. With which record company did Bob release two records in 1969?
10. When Bob was voted King of Comedy in 1962, who was elected as Queen?

QUIZ 77 – RAGBAG 4

1. Who hosted *Here's Harry*?
2. What was the sequel to *The Army Game*?
3. Where was *Para Handy* set?

4. Who was the female lead in *A for Andromeda*?
5. In which year was the Royal Variety Performance first televised?
6. Which diminutive comedian starred in *Bingo Madness*?
7. In 1965 who became the first person to use the F-word on television?
8. Who narrated *Tales of the Riverbank*?
9. Name the two stars of *Hugh and I*.
10. On whose memoirs was *The Valiant Years* based?

QUIZ 78 – ALAN WHICKER

1. In which country was Alan Whicker born?
2. On which TV show did he appear alongside Derek Hart, Cliff Michelmore, Geoffrey Johnson-Smith and Cy Hart?
3. What vehicle was used in the opening titles of *Whicker's World*?
4. Who was the tragic heiress with whom Alan Whicker had a long-running affair?
5. In which year was Alan Whicker voted Television Personality of the Year by BAFTA?
6. Which reclusive billionaire was the subject of one of the first broadcasts of *Whicker's World*?
7. Which comedy show did a send-up of Alan Whicker in which all the members of the team impersonated him at once?
8. To which independent TV company did Alan Whicker move upon leaving the BBC?
9. How many times has Alan Whicker married?
10. On which island does Alan Whicker live?

QUIZ 79 – SOOTY

1. Where did Harry Corbett first see Sooty?
2. How much did Sooty cost Harry Corbett?
3. Why did the BBC worry that Sooty might be introducing sex to children's TV?
4. Which member of the royal family was soaked by Sooty?
5. What was the name of the snake with a Northern accent featured in the show?
6. For how much were Harry Corbett's fingers supposedly insured?
7. In which year did Sooty move from the BBC to ITV?
8. What were the words Sooty whispered to Harry Corbett when he was about to perform a magic trick?
9. How did Harry Corbett sign off each show?
10. True or false: there is a Sooty museum in Lancashire.

PICTURE QUIZ 20

She was a popular presenter for *Blue Peter* in the '60s but in the '80s joined *The Money Programme*. Who is she?

QUIZ 80 – RAGBAG 5

1. Who was the first host of *Points of View*?
2. Who starred in *The Seven Ages of Jim*?
3. Who offered a 'Starter for ten' but cautioned 'No conferring'?
4. What was the profession of Leslie Phillips in *Our Man At St Marks*?
5. In which programme did Bernard Levin call Sir Alec Douglas-Home 'an imbecile' and 'a cretin'?
6. At which football ground was *United* filmed?
7. Which TV series starred Patrick Wymark as John Wilder?
8. Who was the first presenter of *World of Sport*?
9. Who played the title rôle in *Stand Up, Nigel Barton* and *Vote, Vote, Vote for Nigel Barton*?
10. Who was called 'the thinking man's crumpet' for her performance on *Late Night Line-up*?

QUIZ 81 – *CAMBERWICK GREEN* 2

1. What are the names of Micky Murphy's children?
2. Who ran the post office?
3. What was Mr Dagenham's profession?
4. Who swept the village chimneys?
5. Who were the two men in charge of the fort?
6. Who taught geography to the soldier boys?
7. Who looked after the village's vehicles?
8. What was the name of Windy Miller's mill?
9. Who delivered the letters?
10. Who was the doctor?

QUIZ 82 – MARY WHITEHOUSE

1. In which year did the National Viewers' and Listeners' Association launch their first manifesto?
2. What was Mary Whitehouse's occupation when she decided to clean up TV?
3. Against which newspaper did Mary Whitehouse launch a blasphemy suit in the 1970s?
4. Which TV show inspired Mary Whitehouse's campaign?
5. Which comedy trio who rode a tandem built for three did Mary Whitehouse complain were 'too sexually orientated'?
6. Which extremely popular TV show did Mary Whitehouse describe as 'dirty, blasphemous and full of bad language'?
7. Which BBC midweek institution did Mary Whitehouse claim 'dealt dishonestly and offensively with the religious sensitivies of viewers'?
8. Which BBC play did Mary Whitehouse accuse of 'presenting promiscuity as being normal'?
9. Which BBC Director-General thought Mary Whitehouse was 'barking mad'?
10. What was the name of the series that featured a hat-wearing lady called Mrs Smallgood who launched a 'Freedom from Sex' campaign?

QUIZ 83 – *THE LIVER BIRDS*

1. Who created the series?
2. Who wrote the signature tune?
3. Which actresses played the original Liver Birds?
4. Where exactly did the Liver Birds live?
5. What was the name of the character played by Nerys Hughes?
6. What part was played by Mollie Sugden?
7. What animals were reared by Lucien?

PICTURE QUIZ 21

This is Peter Jones. What popular comedy series did he star in?

8. Which member of the Monty Python team was the show's script editor?
9. Who provided the speaking voices in the signature tune?
10. Who joined the show as a Liver Bird in the fourth series?

QUIZ 84 – *THUNDERBIRDS* 3

1. Of what is Lady Penelope particularly frightened?
2. What is Parker's first name?
3. What is the name of the robot invented by Brains?
4. What colour is the nosecone of *Thunderbird 1*?
5. In which pod is the Mole housed?
6. How did Lady Penelope meet Parker?
7. What colour are Brains's spectacle frames?
8. What name did Lady Penelope use as a lounge singer in *That Dangerous Game*?
9. Over which shoulder do the brothers wear their sashes?
10. How many episodes of the show were made?

53

PICTURE QUIZ 22

It shouldn't be too difficult to identify this well-known comedian.

QUIZ 85 – THE AVENGERS 2

1. What was the unlikely name of Steed's boss?
2. Who played the boss?
3. What kind of car did Steed drive?
4. What was Steed's address?
5. What was the profession of Emma Peel's husband?
6. In what subject did Cathy Gale achieve her PhD?
7. What was the name of Steed's dog during the Cathy Gale period?
8. Who originally composed the show's theme tune?
9. What was Emma Peel's maiden name?
10. Who lived at 9, Primrose Crescent?

QUIZ 86 – EUROVISION SONG CONTEST

1. In which year was the Contest first held in the U.K.?
2. Who was the first U.K. winner?

PICTURE QUIZ 23

An actress who became well-known in *The Rag Trade*. Who is she?

3. With which song?
4. Which country won the Contest most times in the '60s?
5. Who represented the U.K. the most times in the '60s?
6. Where did Cliff Richard finish in 1968 with *Congratulations*?
7. Who represented the U.K. with *I Belong*?
8. How many times was the Contest held in the U.K. during the '60s?
9. Who sang *A Man Without Love*?
10. How many countries tied as winners in 1969?

QUIZ 87 – *STINGRAY* 2

1. What is the name of the headquarters of WASP?
2. What was the name of the beautiful mute Pacifican?
3. What nationality is Troy Tempest?
4. How old is Atlanta Shore?

PICTURE QUIZ 24

He went from Round the Horne to Walmington-on-Sea. Who played Chief ARP Warden Hodges in *Dad's Army*?

5. Who is WASP's relief controller?
6. What is the name of the tame seal?
7. What name is given to Titan's soldiers?
8. In what year is *Stingray* set?
9. For how long can *Stingray* remain at sea?
10. How many knobs are there on Commander Shore's hoverchair?

QUIZ 88 – RAGBAG 6

1. Which eleventh-century magician was played by Geoffrey Bayldon?
2. In which country was *Crane* set?
3. What was the real name of *The Baron*?
4. What was the profession of Jason King of *Department S*?
5. By what name were Craig Sterling, Sharron Macready and Richard Barrett better known?
6. Who played *Biggles* in the show of that name?
7. From which zoo was *Animal Magic* often broadcast?

PICTURE QUIZ 25

Betty Driver played which character in *Coronation Street*?

8. What kind of crimes were investigated by Detective Inspector Gamble and Detective Sergeant Hicks?
9. Who played the lead rôle in *Richard the Lionheart*?
10. What was the first name of Gideon in *Gideon's Way*?

QUIZ 89 – *THE AVENGERS* 3

1. What is Emma Peel's favourite card game?
2. What is the licence plate of Tara's car?
3. What was the name of the first *Avengers* story?
4. What caused the break in filming that resulted in Honor Blackman replacing Ian Hendry?
5. Which *Pink Panther* actor played King Temiphon in the episode *Kill the King*?
6. What happened to Cathy Gale's husband?
7. How old was Cathy Gale?

PICTURE QUIZ 26

A star of *Ready, Steady, Go.* Who is he?

8. Who played Father in the episode *Stay Tuned?*
9. What were Tara King's first words in the show?
10. How did the last episode of *The Avengers* end?

QUIZ 90 – *MAIGRET*

1. Who played the Gallic detective during the '60s?
2. Who created Maigret?
3. Who played Maigret's colleague Lucas?
4. True or false: Maigret smoked cigars.
5. In which city was *Maigret* set?
6. For whom did Maigret work?
7. What kind of hat did Maigret invariably wear?
8. What was Maigret's first name?
9. Who played Mme Maigret?
10. When the show was revived in the late 1980s who took the title rôle?

QUIZ 91 – *SUPERCAR*

1. Who pilots Supercar?
2. What was the location of the secret laboratory which developed Supercar?
3. How many rockets can Supercar fire?
4. Name the two scientists who invented Supercar.
5. Who owns the pet monkey called Mitch?
6. When Mitch falls ill, what is the name of the only substance that can cure him?
7. What is the name of Masterspy's righthand man?
8. What does the 'Clear-vu' system do?
9. When Scotland Yard calls in the Supercar team to help solve a series of bank robberies, who is discovered to be behind the thefts?
10. What is the name of the pirate who became involved in a life-and-death struggle with Supercar?

QUIZ 92 – *CALLAN*

1. Who created the show?
2. What was Callan's first name?
3. What was his profession?
4. Under what umbrella title was the show first broadcast?
5. What was the first episode called?
6. What is the codename given to Callan's superiors?
7. How did each show open?
8. What was the nickname of Callan's sidekick?
9. Who played him?
10. What was the subtitle given to the last few episodes of the show?

QUIZ 93 – *TOP OF THE POPS*

1. Who introduced the first show?
2. From where was it broadcast?
3. Who was the first artist to appear?
4. Who were the four DJs who alternated presenting the show for the first three years?
5. Who was the first record spinner?
6. Who hosted the second broadcast of the show?
7. On what date was the first show broadcast?
8. When backing tapes were introduced who provided backing vocals?
9. What was the name of the first dance troupe to appear on the show?
10. The famous theme tune was probably a version of a Led Zeppelin song but what was it called?

QUIZ 94 – TRUMPTON 2

1. Who is the chief fire officer?
2. How many firemen descend the pole?
3. How did each episode begin?
4. Who owned yappy dogs?
5. What were the names of the dogs?
6. What stands in the town square?
7. What kind of flower does the Mayor wear in his buttonhole?
8. Who is the town clockmaker?
9. Of what county is Trumpton the capital?
10. In which year was *Trumpton* originally broadcast?

QUIZ 95 – COMPACT

1. What was *Compact*?
2. Who played the heart-throb Ian Harmon?
3. Who created the show?
4. On which days was the show broadcast?
5. Why did an archbishop complain about the show?
6. What was the name of the first boss?
7. In which year was the first episode broadcast?
8. Who played Gussie?
9. How many characters smoked?
10. A doctor advised that the *Twist* might cause sprains. What name was given to the dance that was featured instead?

QUIZ 96 – DAVID FROST

1. What was the occupation of David Frost's father?
2. What university did David Frost attend?
3. Who called David Frost 'Britain's bravest swordsman' during a heated TV debate?
4. What was the now familiar phrase that came into use following that encounter?
5. What was the name of David Frost's first TV show?
6. Who said of David Frost 'He rose without trace'?
7. In what sport did David Frost turn down the opportunity to turn professional?
8. Which TV company was David Frost instrumental in founding in the late 1960s?
9. Which honour was awarded David Frost in the 1970 New Year Honours List?
10. Which U.S. President was the subject of a major Frost interview in the 1980s?

PICTURE QUIZ 27

Who is the star of *Nearest and Dearest*, above?

QUIZ 97 – *THE FORSYTE SAGA*

1. Who wrote the books on which the series was based?
2. What was the name of the character played by Kenneth More?
3. On which station was the show first broadcast?
4. How much did the series cost?
5. What is the profession of Soames Forsyte?
6. Who raped Irene?
7. Whom did Irene eventually marry?
8. How many times did Kenneth More's character marry?
9. Who played Fleur?
10. Which member of the cast came down with appendicitis, causing the producers to film many scenes out of sequence?

61

QUIZ 98 – *CALL MY BLUFF*

I asked the late Frank Muir for a list of his ten favourite *Call My Bluff* words. The following is what he came up with – can you match the words with their correct definitions?

1.	Norfolk-Howard	a.	Portuguese word for Japanese clergyman
2.	Bonze	b.	A mid-ocean meeting of whalers
3.	Mho	c.	A popular name for a bedbug
4.	Mollie	d.	A fishing fly
5.	Carcel	e.	A unit of electrical conductance, backwards
6.	Frantling	f.	The mating call of the peacock
7.	Bumbolo	g.	An old but renovated top hat
8.	Molocker	h.	A glass flask for sublimating camphor
9.	Minchery	i.	An oil lamp which works by clockwork
10.	Sproat	j.	A dwelling place for nuns

QUIZ 99 – JOHN NOAKES

1. In which year did John join *Blue Peter*?
2. In which branch of the services did John serve?
3. For which comedian did John work as a 'feed'?
4. What once knocked out John during an episode of *Blue Peter*?
5. Where was John born?
6. For what did John first enter *The Guinness Book of Records*?
7. On which alpine bobsleigh run did John have an accident at 80 mph?
8. True or false: John did not get on with Peter Purves.
9. Where did John move to after leaving England?
10. What was the name of the follow-up show (in the '70s) that featured John and Shep?

QUIZ 100 – *SYKES*

1. What was the TV relationship between Eric Sykes and Hattie Jacques?
2. What was the name and nickname of the character played by Deryck Guyler?
3. Who wrote the series?
4. What was the name of their next door neighbour?
5. Who played him?
6. What kind of business did Eric and Hattie originally run?
7. In what road did Eric and Hattie live?
8. Which famous TV commentator appeared on the show when Eric refereed a football match?
9. Part of which unusual animal once hung in Sykes's hall?
10. What was the name of the first episode of the show?

PICTURE QUIZ 28

This is Shane Rimmer. Which character in *Thunderbirds* did he provide the voice for?

QUIZ 101 – GERRY ANDERSON

1. What was the first animated series made by Gerry Anderson?
2. What was the original name of Anderson's film company?
3. What is the name of the appreciation society devoted to the works of Gerry Anderson?
4. How did Anderson describe the voice Francis Matthews used for Captain Scarlet?
5. Which ITV company rejected Anderson's idea for a sci-fi show in the early 1960s before he joined ATV?
6. For which government department did Anderson work in the 1940s?
7. Who was Anderson's first major collaborator?
8. What was the name of the live action film made by Anderson in 1968?
9. What were the puppets for Anderson's first show made of?
10. What anatomical problem in the design of the puppets did Anderson face until the advent of *Captain Scarlet*?

QUIZ 102 – *TILL DEATH US DO PART*

1. When the first show was written (for *Comedy Playhouse*) what was the family surname?
2. Who played Else in that show?
3. What particular insult did Alf regularly apply to Else?
4. What was Alf's occupation?
5. Whose book *Cleaning Up TV* was shown in one episode burning in Alf's fireplace?
6. Which pop group had a hit with *Randy Scouse Git* in tribute to the show?
7. What was the name of Alf's daughter?
8. In one episode, of whom did Alf say Else's hairstyle reminded him?
9. According to Alf, what was Jesus's religion?
10. Who played Mike?

THE '60s TV CALENDAR

1 Anne Aston born, 1948
2 First edition of *Z Cars*, 1962
3 William Mervyn born, 1912
4 First edition of *Face to Face*, 1959
5 First edition of *Softly Softly*, 1966
6 First edition of *This Week*, 1956
7 First edition of *The Avengers*, 1961
8 John Gregson died, 1975
9 Clive Dunn born, 1920
10 Barbara Couper died, 1992
11 Michael Bates died, 1978
12 Michael Aspel born, 1933
13 Ian Hendry born, 1931
14 Warren Mitchell born, 1926
15 Frank Thornton born, 1921
16 First edition of *Sooty*, 1955
17 Philip Latham born, 1929
18 Wilfrid Brambell died, 1985
19 Bryan Pringle born, 1935
20 Neville Buswell born, 1943
21 Benny Hill born, 1924
22 Nyree Dawn Porter born, 1936
23 George Ffitch born, 1929
24 Bamber Gascoigne born, 1935
25 Raymond Baxter born, 1922
26 Michael Bentine born, 1922
27 Brian Rix born, 1924
28 Harry Corbett born, 1918
29 Tony Blackburn born, 1943
30 Roger Tonge born, 1946
31 Carol Hawkins born, 1949

FEBRUARY

1 Peter Sallis born, 1921
2 Hughie Green born, 1920
3 Doris Speed born, 1899
4 Hylda Baker born, 1905
5 Frank Muir born, 1920
6 Leslie Crowther born, 1933

7   Tony Hancock appeared on *Face to Face*, 1960
8   Dame Edith Evans born, 1888
9   First edition of *Gallery*, 1961
10   Joyce Grenfell born, 1910
11   First *Your Life In Their Hands*, 1958
12   Ernest Clark born, 1912
13   Caroline Blakiston born, 1933
14   Mark Eden born, 1928
15   Gerald Harper born, 1929
16   Peter Adamson born, 1930
17   Michael Miles died, 1971
18   Ned Sherrin born, 1931
19   Dick Emery born, 1915
20   Peter Glaze died, 1983
21   James Beck born, 1929
22   Bruce Forsyth born, 1928
23   First edition of *Civilisation*, 1969
24   Dennis Waterman born, 1948
25   Bernard Bresslaw born, 1934
26   Fanny Cradock born, 1909
27   Aimi Macdonald born, 1944
28   Alfred Burke born, 1918
29   Joss Ackland born in the Leap Year of 1928

MARCH

1   Doris Hare born, 1905
2   Jean Metcalfe born, 1923
3   Julian Orchard born, 1930
4   Patrick Moore born, 1923
5   Ann George born, 1903
6   John Noakes born, 1934
7   Richard Vernon born, 1925
8   Margot Bryant born, 1897
9   First edition of *Department S*, 1969
10   Terence Alexander born, 1923
11   Ferdy Mayne born, 1920
12   Arnold Ridley died, 1984
13   Tessie O'Shea born, 1918
14   Bill Owen born, 1915
15   John Gregson born, 1919
16   Last edition of *The Golden Shot*, 1975
17   Patrick Allen born, 1927
18   First edition of *Gideon's Way*, 1965

19 Tommy Cooper born, 1922
20 Sir Michael Redgrave born, 1908
21 Harry H. Corbett died, 1982
22 Wilfrid Brambell born, 1912
23 Jimmy Edwards born, 1920
24 First edition of *Camberwick Green*, 1966
25 Billy Cotton died, 1969
26 Sam Kydd died, 1982
27 Patrick Newell born, 1932
28 Patrick Troughton died, 1987
29 Arthur Negus born, 1903
30 First edition of *The Human Jungle*, 1963
31 Jack Howarth died, 1984

APRIL

1   Carol White born, 1943
2   First edition of *Crane*, 1963
3   Hugh Burden born, 1913
4   Last edition of *Crossroads*, 1988
5   John Le Mesurier born, 1912
6   William Avenell born, 1910
7   Sir David Frost born, 1939
8   Alfie Bass born, 1921
9   Valerie Singleton born, 1937
10 First edition of *The Liver Birds*, 1969
11 Ronald Fraser born, 1930
12 Gerald Flood died, 1989
13 First edition of *Vision On*, 1955
14 Noele Gordon died, 1985
15 Armand Denis died, 1971
16 Joan Bakewell born, 1933
17 Tony Bilbow born, 1932
18 Avril Angers born, 1922
19 Dudley Moore born, 1935
20 Benny Hill found dead, 1992
21 First edition of *Play School*, 1964
22 First edition of *(Late Night) Line-Up*, 1964
23 First edition of *Adam Adamant Lives!*, 1966
24 William Hartnell died, 1975
25 William Roache born, 1932
26 Sid James died, 1976
27 Philip Harben died, 1970
28 Ilona Rogers born, 1942

29 Deryck Guyler born, 1914
30 First edition of *The Troubleshooters*, 1966

MAY

1   Last edition of *Dixon of Dock Green*, 1976
2   Peggy Mount born, 1918
3   Lynn Farleigh born, 1942
4   Terry Scott born, 1927
5   Michael Palin born, 1943
6   Billy Cotton born, 1899
7   Sir Huw Wheldon born, 1913
8   Sir David Attenborough born, 1926
9   Alan Bennett born, 1934
10 Maureen Lipman born, 1946
11 First edition of *The Odd Man*, 1962
12 Tony Hancock born, 1924
13 Last edition of *Not Only...But Also...*, 1970
14 Eric Morecambe born, 1926
15 Lena Martell born, 1940
16 Bernard Braden born, 1916
17 Dennis Potter born, 1935
18 Première of *The Debussy Film*, 1965
19 Madge Hindle born, 1938
20 Betty Driver born, 1920
21 Dandy Nichols born, 1907
22 Rupert Davies born, 1916
23 Nigel Davenport born, 1928
24 Stanley Baxter born, 1926
25 Richard Dimbleby born, 1913
26 Robert Morley born, 1908
27 Reginald Bosanquet died, 1984
28 Dame Thora Hird born, 1911
29 Katie Boyle born, 1926
30 First edition of *The Great War*, 1964
31 Denholm Elliott born, 1922

JUNE

1   Bob Monkhouse born, 1928
2   Milo O'Shea born, 1926
3   Patrick Cargill born, 1918
4   George Reid born, 1939
5   Gilbert Harding born, 1907
6   Arthur Askey born, 1900

7   First edition of *Steptoe & Son*, 1962
8   Millicent Martin born, 1934
9   McDonald Hobley born, 1917
10 Russell Waters born, 1910
11 First edition of *The Man In Room 17*, 1965
12 Peter Jones born, 1920
13 Mary Whitehouse born, 1910
14 First edition of *The Black and White Minstrel Show*, 1958
15 First edition of *Oh, Boy!*, 1958
16 James Bolam born, 1938
17 James Cameron born, 1911
18 Ian Carmichael born, 1920
19 Charlie Drake born, 1925
20 Johnny Morris born, 1916
21 Première of *The Royal Family*, 1969
22 Julian Orchard died, 1979
23 *The Blood Donor* episode of *Hancock* broadcast, 1961
24 Annette Andre born, 1939
25 Tony Hancock committed suicide, 1968
26 Fanny Rowe born, 1913
27 Shirley Ann Field born, 1936
28 Jack Gold born, 1930
29 Ian Bannen born, 1928
30 Lady Isobel Barnett born, 1918

JULY

1   Janet Webb born, 1930
2   Alan Webb born, 1906
3   Ken Russell born, 1927
4   Angela Baddeley born, 1900
5   First edition of *The Expert*, 1968
6   First edition of *Hancock's Half Hour*, 1956
7   Jimmy Edwards died, 1988
8   First edition of *Callan*, 1967
9   First edition of *Dixon of Dock Green*, 1955
10 Mike Pratt died, 1976
11 Reg Varney born, 1916
12 Kenneth More died, 1982
13 Kenneth Clark born, 1903
14 Kenneth Cope born, 1934
15 Derek Griffiths born, 1946
16 Joe Lynch born, 1925
17 Ray Galton born, 1930

18 Michael Medwin born, 1923
19 Hubert Gregg born, 1916
20 Harry Worth died, 1989
21 Queenie Watts born, 1929
22 First edition of *Till Death Us Do Part*, 1965
23 Last edition of *The Likely Lads*, 1966
24 Renee Houston born, 1902
25 Cyril Luckham born, 1907
26 Terry Scott died, 1994
27 Harry Towb born, 1925
28 Simon Dee born, 1934
29 Thames TV went on air, 1968
30 McDonald Hobley died, 1987
31 First edition of *Dad's Army*, 1968

AUGUST

1   Peter Arne murdered, 1983
2   Alan Whicker born, 1921
3   First edition of *The Informer*, 1966
4   Georgina Moon born, 1950
5   John Saxon born, 1935
6   James Beck died, 1973
7   First edition of *It's A Knockout*, 1966
8   Keith Barron born, 1934
9   Reginald Bosanquet born, 1932
10 Kate O'Mara born, 1939
11 Anna Massey born, 1937
12 Fulton Mackay born, 1922
13 Alfred Hitchcock born, 1899
14 Victor Sylvester died, 1978
15 Jim Dale born, 1935
16 Harry Corbett died, 1989
17 First edition of *Stars On Sunday*, 1969
18 Willie Rushton born, 1937
19 Fyfe Robertson born, 1902
20 Yootha Joyce born, 1927
21 Barry Foster born, 1930
22 Honor Blackman born, 1925
23 Julia Lockwood born, 1941
24 Yootha Joyce died, 1980
25 Richard Greene born, 1918
26 Jane Merrow born, 1941
27 Margery Mason born, 1920

28 Michaela Denis born, 1914
29 Richard Attenborough born, 1923
30 Rita Webb died, 1981
31 Roy Castle born, 1932

SEPTEMBER

1   Violet Carson born, 1898
2   Derek Fowlds born, 1937
3   Pauline Collins born, 1940
4   Dinsdale Landen born, 1932
5   Bill Fraser died, 1987
6   Bernie Winters born, 1932
7   Alan Browning died, 1979
8   Jack Rosenthal born, 1931
9   First edition of *Nationwide*, 1969
10 Gwen Watford born, 1927
11 Bill Simpson born, 1931
12 Freddie Jones born, 1927
13 Jacqueline Bissett born, 1944
14 First edition of *Supercar*, 1961
15 First edition of *Knight Errant*, 1960
16 James Montgomery born, 1945
17 Pat Phoenix died, 1986
18 Petra died, 1977
19 Pete Murray born, 1925
20 Roy Kinnear died, 1988
21 Jill Browne born, 1937
22 Arthur Lowe born, 1915
23 First edition of *Bootsie & Snudge*, 1960
24 Sandra Payne born, 1944
25 Ronnie Barker born, 1929
26 Leonard Sachs born, 1909
27 Gordon Honeycombe born, 1936
28 Last episode of *R3*, 1965
29 First edition of *Captain Scarlet and The Mysterons*, 1967
30 First edition of *Thunderbirds*, 1965

OCTOBER

1   Sandy Gall born, 1927
2   First edition of *Points of View*, 1961
3   First edition of *Zero One*, 1962
4   First edition of *The Saint*, 1962

5   Barbara Kelly born, 1923
6   First edition of *Chigley*, 1969
7   Richard Caldicott born, 1908
8   Bill Maynard born, 1928
9   Donald Sinden born, 1923
10 Nicholas Parsons born, 1923
11 Jean Alexander born, 1925
12 Magnus Magnusson born, 1929
13 Wilfred Pickles born, 1904
14 Roger Moore born, 1927
15 Keith Fordyce born, 1928
16 Max Bygraves born, 1922
17 Graham Haberfield died, 1975
18 Leo G. Carroll born, 1892
19 Bernard Hepton born, 1925
20 Patrick Wymark died, 1970
21 Leonard Rossiter born, 1926
22 Last edition of *The Invisible Man*, 1961
23 Anna Palk born, 1941
24 Jack Warner born, 1894
25 Tony Franciosa born, 1928
26 Shaw Taylor born, 1924
27 Last edition of *Riviera Police*, 1965
28 Eddie Waring died, 1986
29 First edition of *Hadleigh*, 1969
30 Dickie Henderson born, 1922
31 Sir Jimmy Savile born, 1926

NOVEMBER

1   Michael Denison born, 1915
2   First edition of *Crossroads*, 1964
3   Première of *Up the Junction*, 1965
4   Dickie Valentine born, 1929
5   Eamonn Andrews died, 1987
6   Donald Churchill born, 1930
7   Derek Francis born, 1923
8   Ken Dodd born, 1927
9   First edition of *Braden's Week*, 1968
10 Last episode of *Counterstrike*, 1969
11 Première of *Elgar*, 1962
12 First edition of *Sir Francis Drake*, 1961
13 First edition of *Not So Much A Programme, More A Way Of Life*, 1964

14   Malcolm Muggeridge died, 1990
15   John Le Mesurier died, 1983
16   Arthur Askey died, 1982
17   Peter Cook born, 1937
18   Andrea Allen born, 1946
19   Arthur Haynes died, 1966
20   Harry Worth born, 1917
21   Ted Ray born, 1907
22   Rupert Davies died, 1976
23   First edition of *Dr Who*, 1963
24   First edition of *That Was The Week That Was*, 1962
25   Ann Davies born, 1934
26   Pat Phoenix born, 1923
27   Robert Dougall born, 1913
28   Première of *1984*, 1965
29   Irene Handl died, 1987
30   Joyce Grenfell died, 1979

DECEMBER

1   Keith Michell born, 1928
2   Marty Feldman died, 1982
3   Armand Denis born, 1897
4   Jimmy Jewel born, 1909
5   Last edition of *Mr Rose*, 1968
6   Jonathan King born, 1944
7   Last edition of *Jacks and Knaves*, 1961
8   Mike Scott born, 1932
9   First edition of *Coronation Street*, 1960
10   Harry Fowler born, 1926
11   Michael Robbins died, 1992
12   First edition of *All Our Yesterdays*, 1960
13   First edition of *Jackanory*, 1965
14   Janette Scott born, 1938
15   Isobel Black born, 1943
16   Ronald Allen born, 1930
17   Robert Robinson born, 1927
18   Last edition of *The Informer*, 1967
19   Eamonn Andrews born, 1922
20   Jess Yates born, 1918
21   Bill Simpson died, 1986
22   Richard Dimbleby died, 1965
23   Last edition of *Ready, Steady, Go*, 1966
24   Ian Hendry died, 1984

25 Noele Gordon born, 1919
26 Violet Carson died, 1983
27 Last edition of *Sentimental Agent*, 1963
28 Bernard Youens born, 1914
29 David Nixon born, 1919
30 Andy Stewart born, 1933
31 Jack Hargreaves born, 1911

FURTHER READING

Although this is by no means a comprehensive list of works consulted in the preparation of this volume, readers who are interested in a particular programme or person may find the following books to be of some use.

Jean Alexander

The Other Side Of The Street – The Autobiography of Jean Alexander – Jean Alexander (Luton: Lennard Books, 1989)

Eamonn Andrews

Eamonn Andrews His Life – Gus Smith (London: W. H. Allen & Co. Ltd, 1988)

Eamonn Andrews – Tom Brennand (London: Weidenfeld & Nicolson, 1989)

Michael Aspel

Polly Wants A Zebra – Michael Aspel (London: Weidenfeld & Nicolson, 1974)

The Avengers

The Complete Avengers – Dave Rogers (London: Boxtree, 1989)

Ronnie Barker

Dancing In The Moonlight – Ronnie Barker (London: Hodder & Stoughton, 1993)

Tony Blackburn

'The Living Legend', An Autobiography – Tony Blackburn as told to Cheryl Garnsey (London: W. H. Allen & Co. Ltd, 1985)

Blue Peter

Blue Peter The Inside Story – Biddy Baxter and Edward Barnes (Letchworth: Ringpress Books, 1989)

Reginald Bosanquet

Let's Get Through Wednesday, My 25 Years with ITN – Reginald Bosanquet with Wallace Reyburn (London: Michael Joseph Ltd, 1980)

Captain Scarlet and The Mysterons

Captain Scarlet and The Mysterons – Chris Drake and Graeme Bassett (London: Boxtree, 1993)

John Cleese
Cleese Encounters – Jonathan Margolis (London: Chapmans, 1992)

Coronation Street
The Real Coronation Street – Ken Irwin (London: Corgi Books, 1970)

Coronation Street: Early Days – H. V. Kershaw (St Albans, Mayflower, 1976)

Trouble At The Rovers – H. V. Kershaw (St Albans, Mayflower, 1976)

Elsie Tanner Fights Back – H. V. Kershaw (St Albans, Mayflower, 1977)

The Street Where I Live – H. V. Kershaw (London: Granada, 1981)

Coronation Street 25 Years – Graham Nown (London: Ward Lock, 1985)

Coronation Street – Jack Tiner (London: Octopus Books, 1985)

Coronation Street The Inside Story – Bill Podmore (London: Macdonald & Co. Ltd, 1990)

Coronation Street Celebrating 30 Years – Graeme Kay (London: Boxtree, 1992)

Coronation Street Classics, The Ogdens – Daran Little (London: Boxtree, 1993)

Coronation Street Classics, Elsie Tanner – Daran Little (London: Boxtree, 1992)

Weatherfield Life – Daran Little and Bill Hill (London: Boxtree, 1992)

Life & Times At The Rover's Return – Daran Little (London: Boxtree, 1993)

Dad's Army
Dad's Army, The Making of a Television Legend – Bill Pertwee (Newton Abbot, David & Charles, 1989)

Danger Man
Danger Man – Dave Rogers (London: Boxtree, 1989)

Richard Dimbleby
Richard Dimbleby – Jonathan Dimbleby (London, Hodder & Stoughton, 1975)

Dr Who
Dr Who The Key To Time – Peter Haining (London: W. H. Allen & Co. Ltd, 1984)

Charlie Drake
Drake's Progress – Charlie Drake (London: Robson Books, 1986)

David Frost
David Frost – Willie Frischauer (London: Michael Joseph, 1972)

An Autobiography Part 1, From Congregation to Audience – David Frost (London: HarperCollins, 1993)

Noele Gordon
My Life At Crossroads – Noele Gordon (London: W.H. Allen & Co. Ltd, 1975)

Hughie Green

Opportunity Knocked – Hughie Green (London: Frederick Muller, 1965)

Tony Hancock

Tony Hancock – Philip Oakes (London: Woburn-Futura, 1975)

Tony Hancock 'Artiste' – Roger Wilmut (London: Methuen London, 1983)

Lady Don't Fall Backwards – Joan Le Mesurier (London: Sidgwick & Jackson, 1988)

Gilbert Harding

Along My Line – Gilbert Harding (London: Beacon Books, 1957)

Benny Hill

The Benny Hill Story – John Smith (London: W. H. Allen & Co. Ltd, 1988)

Saucy Boy, The Life Story of Benny Hill – Leonard Hill (London: Grafton Books, 1990)

The Real Benny Hill – Margaret Forwood (London: Robson Books, 1992)

Benny The True Story – Dennis Kirkland with Hilary Bonner (London: Smith Gryphon, 1992)

Star Turns, The Life and Times of Benny Hill and Frankie Howerd – Barry Took (London: Weidenfeld & Nicolson, 1992)

Frankie Howerd

Titter Ye Not!, The Life of Frankie Howerd – William Hall (London: Grafton, 1992)

Star Turns, The Life and Times of Benny Hill and Frankie Howerd – Barry Took (London: Weidenfeld & Nicolson, 1992)

John Le Mesurier

A Jobbing Actor – John Le Mesurier (London: Elm Tree Books, 1984)

Lady Don't Fall Backwards – Joan Le Mesurier (London: Sidgwick & Jackson, 1988)

Patrick Macnee

Blind In One Ear – Patrick Macnee and Marie Cameron (London: Harrap, 1988)

Bob Monkhouse

Crying With Laughter, An Autobiography – Bob Monkhouse (London: Century, 1993)

Monty Python's Flying Circus

The First 20 Years of Monty Python – Kim 'Howard' Johnson (London: Plexus, 1989)

The Life of Python – George Perry (London: Pavilion Books, 1994)

Morecambe & Wise

Eric & Ernie, The Autobiography of Morecambe & Wise – Referee Dennis Holman (London: W. H. Allen & Co. Ltd, 1972)

Arthur Mullard

Oh, Yus. It's Arthur Mullard – Arthur Mullard (London: Everest Books Ltd, 1977)

Pete Murray

One Day I'll Forget My Trousers – Pete Murray and Jeremy Hornsby (London: Everest Books Ltd, 1975)

Pat Phoenix

All My Burning Bridges – Pat Phoenix (London: Arlington Books, 1974)
Love, Curiosity, Freckles and Doubt – Pat Phoenix (London: Arlington Books, 1983)

The Prisoner

The Prisoner – Dave Rogers (London: Boxtree, 1989)

The Saint

The Saint – Tony Mechele and Dick Fiddy (London: Boxtree, 1989)

Sooty

The Secret Life of Sooty – Geoff Tibballs (Letchworth: Ringpress Books, 1990)

Stingray

Stingray – Dave Rogers (London: Boxtree, 1992)

This Is Your Life

This Is Your Life – Roy Bottomley (London: Methuen London, 1993)

Thunderbirds

Thunderbirds Are Go! – John Marriott (London: Boxtree, 1992)

Top of the Pops

The Story of Top of the Pops – Steve Blacknell (Wellingborough: Patrick Stephens Ltd, 1985)

Jack Warner

Jack of All Trades – Jack Warner (London: W. H. Allen, 1975)

Alan Whicker

Within Whicker's World – Alan Whicker (London: Elm Tree Books/Hamish Hamilton Ltd, 1982)

Carol White

Carol Comes Home – Carol White with Clifford Thurlow (London: NEL, 1982)

Mary Whitehouse

So Who Does She Think She Is? – Mary Whitehouse (London: NEL, 1971)
A Most Dangerous Woman – Mary Whitehouse (Tring: Lion, 1982)

ANSWERS

QUIZ 1 NAME THE YEAR 1
1. 1969
2. 1964
3. 1962
4. 1960
5. 1967

QUIZ 2 *THE RAG TRADE*
1. Fenner's Fabrics
2. Peter Jones
3. Ronald Chesney & Ronald Wolfe
4. Miriam Karlin
5. Peter Jones and Miriam Karlin
6. Reg
7. Sheila Hancock (Carole)
8. Esme Cannon
9. Button holes
10. 'Everybody out!'

QUIZ 3 DAVID NIXON
1. Norman Wisdom
2. London
3. *What's My Line?*
4. *Sugar & Spice*
5. Basil Brush
6. Eamonn Andrews
7. Buttons
8. 3
9. Ronnie Aldrich
10. 37 weeks

QUIZ 4 *PINKY & PERKY*
1. Pinky wore pink and Perky blue
2. Perky
3. *We Belong Together*
4. A fox
5. Conchita
6. PPC TV
7. Ambrose
8. Morton
9. John Slater
10. 1963

QUIZ 5 *DAD'S ARMY* 1
1. False. It was especially written for the show by Jimmy Perry.
2. Bud Flanagan. It was his last professional engagement.
3. Lance Cpl Jones's lady friend
4. Greengrocer
5. Elizabeth
6. It was an in-joke referring to the show's creator David Croft and Jimmy Perry
7. Private Fraser
8. Walmington-on-Sea
9. Captain Square
10. He was allergic to corned beef.

QUIZ 6 RICHARD DIMBLEBY
1. Prince Philip
2. David Lloyd George, known as the Welsh Wizard
3. France
4. *Panorama*
5. CBE
6. *Down Your Way*
7. Belsen
8. *Richmond & Twickenham Times*
9. Westminster Abbey
10. Cancer

QUIZ 7 ADVENTURES OF ROBIN HOOD

Answer: 11

Will Scarlett
Little John
Much
Sheriff
Alan A'Dale
Friar Tuck
Rypon
Sir Falke
Sir William
Maid Marion
Seneschal

W	E	L	A	D	A	N	A	L	A		S
S	I	R	W	I	L	L	I	A	M		E
		L	I	T	T	L	E	J	O	H	N
K			L								E
C				S				E			S
U					C		K				C
T						A	L				H
R	M	A	I	D	M	A	R	I	O	N	A
A	U				F			L			L
I	C			R	Y	P	O	N	E		
R	H	I								T	
F	S	H	E	R	I	F	F				T

QUIZ 8 AMERICAN RAGBAG 1

1. NCC 1701
2. He was responsible for putting more men behind bars than any other lawyer
3. Doorknobs
4. By counting the roses on the wallpaper
5. Fort Courage
6. *Gidget*
7. 7
8. Lisa Douglas
9. The Munsters
10. 8 million

QUIZ 9 *CORONATION STREET* 1

1. Tony Warren
2. May Hardman
3. False
4. Ena Sharples, Minnie Caldwell and Martha Longhurst
5. David
6. Irma Ogden
7. Eric Spear
8. Peter Noone
9. Harry Hewitt and Concepta Riley
10. Kenneth Cope

QUIZ 10 *DR WHO* 1

1. Gallifrey
2. Time And Relative Dimensions In Space
3. His granddaughter, Susan Foreman
4. Skaro
5. Terry Nation
6. Peter Purves
7. Cybermen
8. 1966
9. United Nations Intelligence Taskforce
10. Nicholas Courtney

QUIZ 11 RAGBAG 1

1. Peter Cook and Dudley Moore
2. *On The Braden Beat*
3. Frank Muir and Robert Morley
4. The Gallery
6. Kiki
7. Snowy
8. Jones the Steam
9. *Play School*

5. With the words 'Keep 'em peeled'   10. *Thank Your Lucky Stars*

QUIZ 12 *THE SAGA OF NOGGIN THE NOG*

Answer: There are seven characters:

Noggin the Nog
Nogbad the Bad
The Graculus
Nooka
Thor Nogson
Olaf the Lofty
Prince Knut

N											
	O										
N	O	G	G	I	N	T	H	E	N	O	G
		B									
		G	R	A	C	U	L	U	S		
		E			D		T	U	N	K	E
A	H				T						C
K	T					H					N
O	Y	T	F	E	L		E				I
O	L	A	F	T	H	E			B		R
N										A	P
T	H	O	R	N	O	G	S	O	N		D

QUIZ 13 *THE AVENGERS* 1

1. *Police Surgeon*
2. Ian Hendry
3. Martin King
4. *Kinky Boots*
5. Julie Stevens
6. Jackie Pallo
7. Because she had man appeal – m' appeal!
8. Michael Gough
9. Peter Cushing
10. Linda Thorson

QUIZ 14 *CHIGLEY*

1. Mr Creswell
2. Lord Belborough
3. Mr Brackett
4. Bessie
5. Mr Rumpling
6. Trumptonshire
7. Gordon Murray
8. Brian Cant
9. 13
10. With a dance held by the factory workers

QUIZ 15 *CAMBERWICK GREEN* 1

1. Gordon Murray
2. With a clown turning a screen, followed by a music box containing that episode's character. ('Here is a box, a musical box, wound up and ready to play...')
3. Brian Cant
4. Mrs Honeyman
5. Windy Miller
6. Six
7. Pippin Fort
8. 452
9. Packet
10. Trumptonshire

QUIZ 16 *CAPTAIN SCARLET AND THE MYSTERONS* 1

1 f
2 j
3 i
4 b
5 g
6 c
7 d
8 h
9 e
10 a

79

QUIZ 17 *THUNDERBIRDS* 1

1. They were among the first five Americans in space – Alan (Shepard), John (Glenn), Scott (Carpenter), Gordon (Cooper), Virgil (Grissom)
2. Hiram K. Hackenbacker
3. Pink Rolls Royce
4. FAB 1
5. The Hood
6. Kyrano
7. 6
8. Virgil
9. Scott
10. She died giving birth to Alan

QUIZ 18 RAGBAG 2

1. France
2. Francis Matthews
3. DIY
4. Keith Fordyce & Cathy McGowan
5. Shirley Abicair
6. Ray Martine
7. Armand and Michaela Denis
8. Tony Holland
9. Graham Kerr
10. Gerald Campion

QUIZ 19 *MONTY PYTHON'S FLYING CIRCUS* 1

1. Terry Gilliam
2. *Liberty Bell March*
3. Terry Jones
4. Terry Gilliam
5. Norwegian Blue
6. Carol Cleveland
7. 5th October 1969
8. Michael Palin
9. Eric Idle
10. John Cleese

QUIZ 20 *PLAY SCHOOL*

1. Joy Whitby
2. BBC2
3. Derek Griffiths
4. Cuckoo
5. Jemima
6. *Playaway*
7. Gordon Rollings
8. Round, square and arched
9. Poppy
10. Big Ted and Little Ted

QUIZ 21 *CROSSROADS*

1. Tony Hatch
2. The Midland Road
3. 3
4. Dangerous driving
5. 'Crossroads Motel, may I help you?'
6. Jill
7. Amy Turtle
8. Hawkins
9. David Hunter
10. Roger Tonge (Sandy Richardson)

QUIZ 22 TONY HANCOCK

1. Anthony John Hancock
2. Hancock was writing them himself in his sleep
3. Patrick Cargill and June Whitfield
4. *Educating Archie*
5. 23 Railway Cuttings, East Cheam; and Earl's Court
6. *Lady Don't Fall Backwards*
7. Kenneth Williams
8. Homburg
9. Twice
10. Sydney

QUIZ 23 *DR FINLAY'S CASEBOOK*

1. Janet
2. 'Arden House'
3. Tannochbrae
4. A. J. Cronin
5. Alan
6. 1928
7. Dr Angus Cameron
8. Mistress Niven
9. Anthony Valentine
10. 1913 Sunbeam

QUIZ 24 *THAT WAS THE WEEK THAT WAS*

1. Ned Sherrin
2. Millicent Martin
3. Gerald Kaufman
4. *TW3*
5. Bernard Levin
6. Because it was an election year (1964) and the BBC feared the show might influence the result
7. Richard Ingrams
8. Lance Percival
9. John Bird
10. Never

QUIZ 25 *DANGER MAN*

1. NATO
2. Washington, D.C.
3. Patrick McGoohan
4. Ralph Smart
5. None. McGoohan excised all references to romance from the script.
6. *Secret Agent*
7. Andrew Faulds
8. 731 HOP
9. World Travel
10. M9

QUIZ 26 *CORONATION STREET* 2

1. Alf Roberts and Albert Tatlock
2. Frank Barlow
3. Spiros Papagopolous
4. Ivan and Linda Cheveski
5. Elliston's PVC factory
6. Annie Walker
7. Ena Sharples
8. With his murder
9. He was killed in a car crash
10. The Orinoco Club

QUIZ 27 *THUNDERBIRDS* 2

1. 2026
2. 15,000 mph
3. Shane Rimmer
4. John
5. Gordon
6. Alan
7. Virgil
8. Creighton-Ward
9. Burglary
10. Sylvia Anderson

QUIZ 28 *THE LIKELY LADS*

1. Electric components factory
2. Terry Collier and Bob Ferris
3. Newcastle
4. Rupert Bear
5. The army
6. He was rejected because he had flat feet
7. James Bolam (Terry) and Rodney Bewes (Bob)
8. Dick Clement and Ian La Frenais
9. They drank real Brown Ale
10. *Whatever Happened to The Likely Lads?*

QUIZ 29 SID JAMES

1. Johannesburg
2. *George and the Dragon*
3. Handyman and housekeeper respectively in a stately home
4. Boxing
5. *Black Memory*
6. 1960
7. *Carry on Constable*
8. 19
9. *Citizen James*
10. Diana Coupland

QUIZ 30 NAME THE YEAR 2

1. 1961
2. 1966
3. 1968
4. 1965
5. 1963

QUIZ 31 *THE PRISONER*

1. Portmeirion
2. No 6
3. Lotus 7
4. Leo McKern
5. 'In the Village'
6. Patrick McGoohan
7. Six of One
8. It has never been revealed although many fans of the show have suggested John Drake, the character played by McGoohan in *Danger Man*.
9. 19th March 1928 (which happens to be Patrick McGoohan's birthday)
10. *Fall Out*

QUIZ 32 *IT'S A KNOCKOUT*

1. David Vine and Eddie Waring
2. (a) Blackpool
3. *Jeux Sans Frontières*
4. Arthur Ellis
5. Guido Pancaldi, Genaro Olivieri
6. Fils rouge
7. Stuart Hall
8. 1966
9. *Almost Anything Goes*
10. The Princess Royal and the Duke and Duchess of York

QUIZ 33 *CATCHPHRASE*

1. David Frost
2. Basil Brush
3. Ken Dodd
4. Dick Emery as Clarence
5. Cyril Fletcher
6. Norman Vaughan
7. Hylda Baker (about Cynthia)
8. Frankie Howerd
9. Hughie Green
10. Bruce Forsyth

QUIZ 34 *CORONATION STREET* 3

1. Leonard Swindley
2. Rosamund Street
3. 2nd Class BA Honours in History and English
4. For taking part in an anti-Vietnam War march
5. Susan by 4 oz. She weighed 5lb 3oz while Peter weighed in at 4lb 11oz
6. 1965
8. Betty Turpin
9. 15 Mawdesley Street

7. Armistead   10. Crabtree

QUIZ 35 JESS YATES

1. The Bishop   6. *The Good Old Days*
2. Manchester (Tyldesley)   7. Hotelier
3. Playing the organ in the Odeon   8. 32 years
4. Children's Film Foundation   9. *How We Used To Live*
5. Littlewoods and Vernons   10. Anthony Valentine

QUIZ 36 *CAPTAIN PUGWASH*

1. *The Black Pig*   6. *The Hornblower*
2. Cut-Throat Jake   7. He was never given a name
3. Tom   8. Willy and Barnabas
4. Peter Hawkins   9. Tom the cabin boy
5. John Ryan   10. Sir Prancelot

QUIZ 37 *JOE 90*

1. McClaine   8. Mrs Ada Harris
2. Nine   9. They activate the brain
3. Brain Impulse Galvanoscope   patterns of whoever has been
    Record And Transfer   copied by BIG RAT
4. Rupert Davies   10. With Joe's tenth birthday
5. World Intelligence Network   party and a series of flash-
6. Sam Loover   backs to his most exciting
7. In his schoolbag   missions.

QUIZ 38 *FIREBALL XL5*

1. 2067   6. *Fireball Junior*
2. Colonel Steve Zodiac   7. Sector 25
3. Venus   8. Lieutenant Ninety
4. 300ft   9. He's a transparent robot
5. Zoonie, a Lazoon   10. Professor Matthew 'Matt'
                                     Matic

QUIZ 39 HARRY H. CORBETT

1. 'Hanything'
2. To distinguish himself from the puppeteer
3. Rangoon   7. OBE
4. Soldier   8. Sheila Steafel
5. Joan Littlewood   9. *Carry on Screaming*
6. *Mr Aitch*   10. 5' 10"

QUIZ 40 *DIXON OF DOCK GREEN*

1. Andy Crawford   6. Beneath a police lamp
2. George   7. Ted Willis
3. *The Blue Lamp*   8. Mary
4. 'Evenin' all'   9. (a) 429
5. *An Ordinary Copper*   10. Paul Eddington

QUIZ 41 *ADAM ADAMANT LIVES!*

1. Edwardian
2. Juliet Harmer
3. Adam Llewellyn De Vere Adamant
4. The Face
5. He was entombed in a block of ice
6. Gerald Harper
7. Kenneth Kendall
8. Ridley Scott
9. None – he was proficient with them all
10. 29

QUIZ 42 *Z CARS*

1. Brian Blessed
2. Newtown and Seaport
3. John Watt and Charlie Barlow
4. James Ellis
5. By listening to police radio while he was in bed with the mumps
6. Colin Welland
7. *Johnny Todd*
8. Douglas Fielding
9. Charlie Barlow
10. Z Victor 1, Z Victor 2

QUIZ 43 *CAPTAIN SCARLET AND THE MYSTERONS* 2

1. Spectrum Pursuit Vehicle
2. The driver sat facing the opposite direction to that which the vehicle was travelling and watched the road ahead via a TV screen.
3. Mars
4. Zero X
5. Captain Scarlet
6. Francis Matthews
7. Captain Magenta
8. Donald Grey
9. The eyes of the Mysterons
10. Retro-metabolism

QUIZ 44 *CORONATION STREET* 4

1. Elsie Tanner
2. None. He was Ken's first wife's uncle.
3. Police sergeant
4. Elsie Lappin
5. His bowls bag and old love letters to Annie
6. 4 – Irma, Trevor, Tony and Sylvia
7. County
8. Paul Cheveski
9. The age gap – he was 21, she 33
10. Ena Sharples

QUIZ 45 *THE MAGIC ROUNDABOUT*

Answer: There are eleven characters. They are:

Dylan	Ermintrude
Mr MacHenry	Dougal
Mr Rusty	Florence
Paul	Basil
Rosalie	Brian

and, of course, Zebedee

D		E	D	U	R	T	N	I	M	R	E
	Y	R	N	E	H	C	A	M	R	M	
	L				D	O	U	G	A	L	
		A									
			N	M							
Z		F	L	O	R	E	N	C	E	E	
E				R						I	
B			L	U	A	P				L	
E		B	A	S	I	L				A	
D				T						S	
E				Y						O	
E						N	A	I	R	B	

QUIZ 46 *THE TROUBLESHOOTERS*

1. *Mogul*
2. Alec Stewart, Peter Thornton
3. Zenith
4. Harry Mayne
5. Bernard Hepton
6. Willy Izzard
7. BP
8. Director of Operations
9. Tom Springfield
10. Margaret Thatcher

QUIZ 47 *MONTY PYTHON'S FLYING CIRCUS* 2

1. He is scared he will slaughter his customers
2. To be a lumberjack
3. He had three buttocks
4. Whizzo Chocolate Company
5. Verity Lambert. Graham Chapman and Eric Idle played Mr Lambert and Mr Verity
6. Hell's Grannies
7. John Cleese
8. 126
9. Because his walk has recently become even sillier
10. Spiny Norman

QUIZ 48 COMMERCIAL BREAK

1. Milky Bar
2. Mary Holland
3. Double Diamond
4. Alan Freeman
5. Smarties
6. Katie Boyle
7. Bernard Miles
8. John Le Mesurier
9. Esso
10. Terence Brook

QUIZ 49 *DAD'S ARMY* 2

1. Private Godfrey
2. Frank
3. Napoleon
4. Mr Yateman
5. Captain Mainwaring
6. Frazer
7. Lance Corporal Jones's
8. Lance Corporal Jones
9. Private Godfrey
10. Because Wilson was Pike's mum's boyfriend and, quite possibly, his father

QUIZ 50 *RANDALL & HOPKIRK (DECEASED)*

1. In a hit and run
2. *My Partner the Ghost*
3. Dave Allen
4. Jean
5. 100 years
6. 1 – Jeff
7. Maida Vale
8. In Loving Memory Marty Hopkirk Faithful Unto Death
9. Steven Randall
10. *The Smile Behind the Veil*

QUIZ 51 *THIS IS YOUR LIFE*

1. Eamonn Andrews
2. Ralph Edwards
3. David Nixon
4. Joe Mercer
7. Danny Blanchflower and Richard Gordon
8. Laurie Johnson
9. Freddie Mills

5. The Beverly Sisters
6. 1964

QUIZ 52 *THE CLANGERS*

Answers:
Iron Chicken
Grannie
Copper
Major
Mother
Brass
Soup Dragon
Tiny
Small

10. Lord Mountbatten

I	R	O	N	C	H	I	C	K	E	N	
					N		I				
		B	O		N						
M	A	J	O	R	G	N					
O					A						
T				R	R	S					
H		G			D		S	M	A	L	L
E		T			P						
R		I			U						
	N				O	R	E	P	P	O	C
Y					S						

QUIZ 53 *DR WHO* 2

1. Frazer Hines
2. William Russell
3. The TARDIS is supposed to be able to assume a shape to blend into its surroundings. Unfortunately, the machine has been repaired once too often and has now broken, hence it is stuck as a police box. (In fact, the producers spent half their budget on the box and couldn't afford to replace it.)
4. Ron Grainer
5. *An Unearthly Child*
6. 23rd November 1963
7. The Gojos
8. The Beatles
9. Regeneration
10. Patrick Troughton

QUIZ 54 *MAGPIE*

1. Sorrow
2. Susan Stranks, Tony Bastable, Douglas Rae
3. 7
4. Jenny Hanley
5. Susan Stranks
6. 1968
7. 1980
8. A secret never to be told
9. It was a look at historical events that had happened that particular day and it was presented by Tony Bastable.
10. Thames TV

QUIZ 55 *MONTY PYTHON'S FLYING CIRCUS* 3

1. Half an inch
2. *Jerusalem*
3. Lion-taming
4. He has a lion-taming hat
5. Chartered accountancy
6. It was nailed there
7. Spam
8. Harold
9. None
10. Sandwiches

QUIZ 56 *PLEASE SIR!*

1. 5C
2. Frankie Abbot
3. Privet
6. Penny Spencer
7. Eric Duffy
8. Dennis Dunstable

4. Desert Rats
5. Maureen

9. Miss (Doris) Ewell
10. *The Fenn Street Gang*

QUIZ 57 *CATHY COME HOME*

1. Carol White, Ray Brooks
2. Jeremy Sandford
3. Ken Loach
4. It was improvised with the actors using the dialogue only as a framework
5. SHELTER

6. Housing minister Anthony Greenwood
7. She hitch-hiked
8. 2
9. 1966
10. Delivery driver

QUIZ 58 *BLUE PETER*

1. 1962
2. Patch
3. Valerie Singleton
4. 1965
5. It turned out to be female and its name was changed to Freda

6. 1965, Norway
7. *Barnacle Bill*
8. Jason
9. John Noakes
10. Lulu

QUIZ 59 *CORONATION STREET* 5

1. Bobbie
2. GPO
3. Maison Valerie
4. Walter Potts
5. Jerry Booth
6. Stan Ogden

7. Because Stan Ogden secretly stopped the clock at a hotpot supper
8. Emily Nugent
9. A brain tumour
10. Annie Walker

QUIZ 60 PAT PHOENIX

1. Manchester. St Mary's Hospital to be precise
2. Patricia Frederica Manfield (later Pilkington)
3. She sent a photograph to an agent who couldn't read her name and rang to ask what it was. At the time she was reading a book called *Phoenix Rising* by Marguerite Steen.
4. Alan Browning
5. 1973 in October
6. Tony Warren, creator of *Coronation Street*
7. *Constant Hot Water*
8. False. She was an interminable chain smoker.
9. Labour (the daughter of her last husband is married to Tony Blair).
10. Her last husband, Tony Booth, was one of the stars of the show. By coincidence, he played a character called Pilkington in the ill-fated soap *Albion Market*, produced by Granada, makers of *Coronation Street*.

QUIZ 61 AMERICAN RAGBAG 2

1. Marcia Carol Greg
   Jan Alice Peter
   Cindy Mike Bobby
2. Edward Mulhare
3. As a 1928 Porter (a make of car) in *My Mother the Car*
4. 'Stately Wayne Manor'
5. Perry Mason
6. Kookie
7. A seasick sea serpent
8. Miss Barbara Stanwyck
9. Adam, Hoss, Little Joe
10. 1,000,040 BC

QUIZ 62 *CRACKERJACK*

1. Eamonn Andrews
2. *Double or Drop*
3. Friday, 5 to 5
4. Peter Glaze
5. (b) Lesley Judd
6. Leslie Crowther
7. Jack Douglas and Joe Baker
8. Christine Holmes
9. Crackerjack pencils
10. 'CRACKERJACK'

QUIZ 63 *TRUMPTON* 1

1 f	6 c
2 a	7 b
3 j	8 g
4 h	9 d
5 e	10 i

QUIZ 64 *NEAREST & DEAREST*

1. Pledge's Pure Pickles
2. Hylda Baker and Jimmy Jewel
3. Sister and brother
4. Walter
5. Edward Malin
6. Stan
7. Madge Hindle
8. True. In one episode, she was indignant when Eli suggested she had a fancy man: 'How dare you! Calling your own sister a trombone!' 'You mean strumpet!'
9. Granada
10. Vince Powell and Harry Driver

QUIZ 65 *FOUR FEATHER FALLS*

1. One allowed the dog Dusty to talk, another gave horse Rocky the same power while the third and fourth allowed Tex's guns to swivel at great speed and fire automatically whenever Tex's life was in danger.
2. Nicholas Parsons
3. Michael Holiday
4. Pedro
5. Rocky, Dusty
6. Slim Jim
7. Denison Saloon
8. Kansas
9. Ma Jones
10. Red Scalp

QUIZ 66 DICK EMERY

1. Music hall artistes – Callen & Emery
2. Mandy

3. False: he was often physically sick
4. Ralph Reader
5. The Windmill Theatre
6. Hetty
7. 'Dad, I fink I got it wrong again!'
8. College
9. 5
10. Lampwick

QUIZ 67 *DR WHO* 3

Answer: 21

Barbara	Polly
Ben	Xerons
Cybermen	Sensorite
Dodo	Toymaker
Moroks	Yeti
Davros	Chalren
Jamie	Ice Warriors
Thals	Morpho
Victoria	Delos
Zoe	Daleks
Zarbi	

P		B	A	R	B	A	R	A			I
O			N	E	M	R	E	B	Y	C	
L		S	E	N	S	O	R	I	T	E	
L	M	O	R	O	K	S			R	W	
Y	E	T	I	L		D		V	X	E	A
			A	J	A	M	I	E	K	R	
S	D		H		L	O	C	R	A	R	
O	Z	O	E	C		E	R	T	O	M	I
R	D	N			K	P	O	N	Y	O	
V	O			S	H	R	S	O	R		
A	Z	A	R	B	I	O	I		T	S	
D	E	L	O	S		T	H	A	L	S	

QUIZ 68 RAGBAG 3

1. Hans and Lotte Hass
2. Monica Rose
3. Jonathan Routh
4. Kenneth Wolstenholme
5. Max Robertson
6. John Nettleton
7. Norma Sykes
8. *Public Eye*
9. Michael Bentine
10. *Take A Letter*

QUIZ 69 ARTHUR LOWE

1. Leonard Swindley
2. To join the Merchant Navy but he was let down by his poor eyesight
3. 30
4. *Pardon the Expression*
5. Father Duddleswell
6. Headmaster
7. Derbyshire
8. 1960s
9. *Mr Men*
10. Sergeant-Major

QUIZ 70 *THE GOLDEN SHOT*

1. Canadian
2. 1967
3. Switzerland
4. Carol Dilworth, Andrea Lloyd and Anita Richardson
5. Saturday (It switched to Sunday tea time in 1968)
6. Bernie the Bolt (Actually, there were three Bernies – Derek Young, Alan Bailey and Johnny Baker)
7. Bob Monkhouse
8. Anne Aston
9. ATV
10. Norman Vaughan

QUIZ 71 MORECAMBE & WISE

1. Ernie. He was born on 27th November 1925, while Eric didn't arrive until 14th May 1926.
2. Eric was Bartholomew while Ernie was Wiseman
3. 1941
4. *Running Wild*
5. Mr Preview
6. Shirley Bassey
7. Peter Cushing (he got his money eventually)
8. Three (*The Intelligence Men*, 1964, *That Riviera Touch*, 1965, *The Magnificent Two*, 1966)
9. Glenda Jackson
10. Janet Webb

QUIZ 72 *THE SAINT*

1. ST 1
2. Ivor Dean
3. Volvo P-1800
4. Leslie Charteris
5. An outline figure of a saint
6. 6' 2"
7. Patrick McGoohan
8. Honor Blackman
9. (f) Bernard Youens
10. Roger Moore

QUIZ 73 *STEPTOE & SON*

1. Hercules
2. Albert taught him the woman's steps, so Harold danced backwards in a competition.
3. Ray Galton and Alan Simpson
4. Shepherd's Bush
5. *Comedy Playhouse*
6. Pickled onions
7. Lew Grade
8. A skeleton
9. 'You dirty old man!'
10. Bear

QUIZ 74 *FACE TO FACE*

1. John Freeman
2. Gilbert Harding
3. The death of his mother
4. He was never seen
5. U.S.A.
6. London Weekend Television
7. *The New Statesman*
8. *Person to Person*
9. 2
10. Jeremy Isaacs

QUIZ 75 *STINGRAY* 1

1. 'Stand by for action! Anything can happen in the next half hour.'
2. Gary Miller
3. Troy Tempest
4. World Aquanaut Security Patrol
5. George Lee Sheridan
6. Titan
7. Sam Shore
8. Troy Tempest
9. 3
10. 16

QUIZ 76 BOB MONKHOUSE

1. Jackie Rae
2. Disc jockey
3. *Sunday Night at the London Palladium*
6. *Mad Movies*
7. *Carry on Sergeant*
8. OBE
9. CBS

4. *Candid Camera*
5. Denis Goodwin

10. Hylda Baker

QUIZ 77 RAGBAG 4

1. Harry Worth
2. *Bootsie & Snudge*
3. On a steamer on the Clyde
4. Julie Christie
5. 1960
6. Charlie Drake
7. Kenneth Tynan
8. Johnny Morris
9. Hugh Lloyd and Terry Scott
10. Winston Churchill

QUIZ 78 ALAN WHICKER

1. Egypt
2. *Tonight*
3. A VC-10 moved across tarmac to reveal the words 'Whicker's World' spelled out in huge letters.
4. Olga Deterding
5. 1964
6. John Paul Getty
7. *Monty Python's Flying Circus*
8. Yorkshire TV
9. None
10. Jersey

QUIZ 79 SOOTY

1. In Blackpool, while on holiday
2. *7s. 6d.*
3. When Soo joined the programme, it looked as though she and Sooty were living together
4. Prince Philip
5. Ramsbottom
6. £20,000
7. 1968
8. 'Izzy wizzy, let's get busy'
9. 'Bye-bye, everybody. Bye-bye'
10. False – it is in Shipley, West Yorkshire

QUIZ 80 RAGBAG 5

1. Robert Robinson
2. Jimmy Edwards
3. Bamber Gascoigne, on *University Challenge*
4. Vicar
5. *Not So Much A Programme, More A Way Of Life*
6. Stoke City stadium – Victoria Ground
7. *The Plane Makers*
8. Eamonn Andrews
9. Keith Barron
10. Joan Bakewell

QUIZ 81 *CAMBERWICK GREEN* 2

1. Mary and Paddy
2. Mrs Dingle
3. Salesman
4. Roger Varley
5. Captain Snort and Sergeant-Major Grout
6. Mr Carraway
7. Mr Crockett
8. Colley's Mill
9. Peter Hazel
10. Dr Mopp

QUIZ 82 MARY WHITEHOUSE

1. 1964

2. Schoolteacher (she was responsible for sex education)
3. *Gay News*
4. *Meeting Point*
5. *The Goodies*
6. *Till Death Us Do Part*
7. The Wednesday Play
8. *Up the Junction*
9. Sir Hugh Carleton-Greene
10. *Swizzlewick*

QUIZ 83 *THE LIVER BIRDS*

1. Carla Lane
2. The Scaffold
3. Pauline Collins (Dawn) and Polly James (Beryl Hennessey)
4. Huskisson Street, Liverpool
5. Sandra Hutchinson
6. Mrs Hutchinson, Sandra's mum
7. Rabbits
8. Eric Idle
9. Polly James and Roger McGough
10. Elizabeth Estensen as Carol Boswell

QUIZ 84 *THUNDERBIRDS* 3

1. Mice
2. Aloysius
3. Brainman
4. Red
5. Pod 4
6. He was trying to steal her car
7. Blue
8. Wanda Lamour
9. Left
10. 32

QUIZ 85 *THE AVENGERS* 2

1. Mother
2. Patrick Newell
3. Rolls Royce Silver Ghost, then a Bentley Convertible
4. 5 Westminster Mews, then 3 Stable Mews, both in the City of London
5. Test pilot
6. Anthropology
7. Sheba
8. Johnny Dankworth
9. Knight
10. Tara King

QUIZ 86 *EUROVISION SONG CONTEST*

1. 1960
2. Sandie Shaw
3. *Puppet On A String*
4. France – 3 times
5. Ronnie Carroll
6. 2nd
7. Kathy Kirby
8. 3 times – 1960, 1963, 1968
9. Kenneth McKellar
10. 4

QUIZ 87 *STINGRAY* 2

1. Marineville
2. Marina
3. American
4. 23
5. Sub-Lieutenant John Fisher
6. Oink
7. Aquaphibians
8. 2065
9. 6 months
10. 7

QUIZ 88 RAGBAG 6

1. Catweazle
2. Morocco
6. Neville Whiting
7. Bristol Zoo

3. John Mannering
4. Novelist
5. *The Champions*

8. Fraud (in *Fraud Squad*)
9. Dermot Walsh
10. George

QUIZ 89 *THE AVENGERS* 3

1. Bridge
2. NPW 99F
3. *Hot Snow*
4. There was an Equity strike
5. Burt Kwouk
6. He was killed during the Mau-Mau uprising in Kenya

7. 28–30
8. Iris Russell
9. 'Mother sent me'
10. With Steed, Tara and Mother blasting off into space

QUIZ 90 *MAIGRET*

1. Rupert Davies
2. Georges Simenon
3. Ewen Solon
4. False – he smoked a pipe
5. Paris

6. Sûreté
7. Trilby
8. Jules
9. Helen Shingler
10. Richard Harris

QUIZ 91 *SUPERCAR*

1. Mike Mercury
2. In the Nevada desert
3. Eight
4. Doctor Beaker and Professor Popkiss
5. Jimmy Gibson
6. T'logi plant

7. Zarin
8. It enables the pilot to 'see' through fog, mist, clouds and storms
9. Two Chicago gangsters: Joe and Maxie Hoyle
10. Black Morgan

QUIZ 92 *CALLAN*

1. James Mitchell
2. David
3. Hit man

4. *Armchair Theatre*
5. *A Magnum for Schneider*
6. Hunter

7. A lightbulb swung backwards and forwards before exploding in slow motion at the sound of a gunshot
8. Lonely
9. Russell Hunter
10. *The Richmond Files*

QUIZ 93 *TOP OF THE POPS*

1. Jimmy Savile
2. Manchester
3. The Rolling Stones with *I Wanna Be Your Man*
4. Jimmy Savile, Pete Murray, David Jacobs, Alan Freeman
5. Denise Sampey (then Samantha Juste and Diane Hefforan)

6. Alan Freeman
7. 1st January 1964
8. The Ladybirds
9. The Gojos
10. *Whole Lotta Love*

93

QUIZ 94 *TRUMPTON* 2

1. Captain Flack
2. 6
3. With the Trumpton clock ('Here is the clock, the Trumpton clock, telling the time, sensibly, steadily, never too quickly, never too slowly, telling the time for Trumpton') and the figurines on the clock
4. Miss Lovelace
5. Mitzi, Lulu and Daphne
6. A statue of Queen Victoria
7. A red carnation
8. Mr Platt
9. Trumptonshire
10. 1967

QUIZ 95 *COMPACT*

1. 'A topical magazine for busy women'
2. Ronald Allen
3. Hazel Adair
4. Tuesdays and Thursdays
5. Because a single woman on the show became pregnant
6. Joanne Minster
7. 1962 (9th January)
8. Frances Bennett
9. None
10. *The Method*

QUIZ 96 DAVID FROST

1. Methodist minister
2. Cambridge
3. Emil Savundra
4. Trial by television
5. *Town and Gown* (at Anglia)
6. Kitty Muggeridge
7. Football
8. London Weekend Television
9. OBE
10. Richard Nixon

QUIZ 97 *THE FORSYTE SAGA*

1. John Galsworthy
2. Jolyon Forsyte
3. BBC2
4. £250,000
5. Lawyer
6. Her husband Soames
7. Jolyon, her husband's cousin
8. 3
9. Susan Hampshire
10. Eric Porter

QUIZ 98 *CALL MY BLUFF*

1 c
2 a
3 e
4 b
5 i
6 f
7 h
8 g
9 j
10 d

QUIZ 99 JOHN NOAKES

1. 1965 (December)
2. RAF
3. Cyril Fletcher
4. A 5lb imitation marrow
7. Cresta Run
8. False: they got on extremely well
9. On a boat in Majorca

5. Halifax, West Yorkshire (on 6th March 1934)
6. The first civilian to make a 25,000 ft freefall parachute jump
10. *Go With Noakes*

QUIZ 100 SYKES

1. Brother and sister
2. Name: Constable Turnbull ('Helmet on'). Nickname: Corky ('Helmet off')
3. Eric Sykes (although the first episode was written by Johnny Speight)
4. Mr Brown
5. Richard Wattis
6. A sweetshop
7. Sebastopol Terrace
8. Kenneth Wolstenholme
9. An elephant's head and trunk
10. *Sykes and a Telephone*

QUIZ 101 GERRY ANDERSON

1. *The Adventures of Twizzle*
2. A.P. Films
3. Fanderson
4. 'His Cary Grant voice'
5. Granada
6. The Ministry of Information
7. Arthur Poviz, hence A.P. Films
8. *Doppelganger* (also known as *Far Side of the Sun*). Some of the sets, models and actors were reused in the 1970 television series *UFO*.
9. Papier mâché
10. The heads of the puppets contained electronic equipment to make the mouths synchronise with the voices (the technique Anderson called Supermarionation), but this unfortunately meant that the heads had to be out of proportion with the bodies.

QUIZ 102 *TILL DEATH US DO PART*

1. Ramsey
2. Gretchen Franklin
3. 'Silly old moo'
4. Docker
5. Mary Whitehouse
6. The Monkees (The BBC, needless to say, banned it)
7. Rita
8. Ken Dodd
9. Church of England
10. Tony Booth

ANSWERS TO PICTURE QUIZZES

1. Francis Matthews (who played Paul Temple)
2. Bob Holness
3. Alexandra Bastedo (from *The Champions*)
4. Una Stubbs (From *Till Death Us Do Part*)
5. Geoffrey Bayldon (*Catweazle* and *Worzel Gummidge*)
6. Bernard Braden
7. Soo
8. Mary Whitehouse
9. John Eric Bartholomew and Ernest Wiseman

10. Wrestling
11. Nicholas Parsons
12. 1959
13. (a) The origin of the name is as bizarre as the programme. Original proposals were mainly random or surreal and included *Gwen Dibley's Flying Circus*, *Vaseline Review* and *Owl-Stretching Time*. The first of these was preferred, with John Cleese suggesting *Python* instead of *Gwen Dibley*, to which Eric Idle added *Monty*. This last name was adopted from that of a pub regular that Idle knew, about whom fellow drinkers would enquire 'Monty in yet?', 'Anyone see Monty?', and the like [Thanks to Adrian Room for supplying this information. If you got any of it right, you did well.]   (b) It is 'Liberty Bell', by John Sousa
14. Honor Blackman, who played Cathy Gale
15. Gerald Harper
16. Jamie
17. Richard Wagner
18. June Whitfield
19. Ned Sherrin
20. Valerie Singleton
21. *The Rag Trade*
22. Eric Sykes
23. Sheila Hancock
24. Bill Pertwee
25. Betty Turpin
26. Keith Fordyce
27. Jimmy Jewel
28. Scott Tracy